Semimartingales and their Stochastic Calculus on Manifolds

COLLECTION DE LA CHAIRE AISENSTADT

Fondateur : Lucien Le Cam, Université de Berkeley

Directeur : Anatole Joffe, directeur du Centre de recherches mathématiques de l'Université de Montréal

Dans la même collection

Robert Hermann, *Physical Aspects of Life Group Theory,* 1974

Mark Kac, *Quelques problèmes mathématiques en physique statistique,* 1974

S. R. de Groot, *la Transformation de Weyl et la fonction de Wigner : une forme alternative de la mécanique quantique,* 1975

Jacques Louis Lions, *Sur quelques questions d'analyse, de mécanique et de contrôle optimal,* 1976

Donald E. Knuth, *Mariages stables et leurs relations avec d'autres problèmes combinatoires,* 1976/1981

R. Tyrrell Rockafellar, *la Théorie des sous-gradients et ses applications à l'optimisation. Fonctions convexes et non convexes,* 1979

Yuval Ne'eman, *Symétries, jauges et variétés de groupes,* 1979

Cette collection est consacrée à la publication des conférences données, depuis 1970, au Centre de recherches mathématiques de l'Université de Montréal, dans le cadre de la Chaire Aisenstadt. C'est grâce à la générosité de Monsieur André Aisenstadt, docteur en physique théorique de l'Université de Zurich, que le Centre de recherches mathématiques peut inviter des chercheurs prestigieux et publier, aux Presses de l'Université de Montréal, le texte de leur conférence.

Semimartingales and their Stochastic Calculus on Manifolds

Laurent Schwartz

Edited by I. ISCOE

1984
Les Presses de l'Université de Montréal
C.P. 6128, succ. «A», Montréal (Québec), Canada H3C 3J7

ISBN 2-7606-0660-0

Dépôt légal, 2e trimestre 1984 — Bibliothèque nationale du Québec

AVANT PROPOS

Le présent livre, rédigé par Monsieur Ian Iscoe, est un développement des leçons que j'ai données dans le cadre de la Chaire Aisenstadt à l'Université de Montréal en avril et août 1982.

Bien des questions traitées ici sont exposées dans des ouvrages français tels que les Séminaires de probabilités de Strasbourg édités chez Springer-Verlag, y inclus mes propres écrits dans cette collection (voir bibliographie plus loin); c'est pourquoi une rédaction de ces leçons en français aurait présenté un intérêt limité. Au contraire, les concepts développés ici avec des semi-martingales générales non nécessairement liées au mouvement brownien ne sont pas usuelles. De plus, leur définition intrinsèque en géométrie différentielle n'est pas courante dans la littérature anglo-américaine; cette publication arrive donc tout à fait à propos.

Je remercie vivement le Docteur André Aisenstadt, le Centre de recherche de mathématiques appliquées, son Directeur Monsieur A. Joffe pour leur hospitalité et leur accueil.

Monsieur I. Iscoe en particulier a toute ma reconnaissance pour le soin qu'il a apporté à la rédaction de ce volume qui contient des compléments que je n'ai pas eu le loisir de présenter dans l'exposé oral.

Finalement, je remercie Madame F. Houle-Miller pour son excellent travail de typographie.

L.S.

TABLE OF CONTENTS

TABLE DES MATIERES

INTRODUCTION

Ce livre expose la théorie des semi-martingales et du calcul stochastique qui leur est associé, dans les espaces vectoriels réels de dimension finie et sur les variétés. Il est basé sur deux séries de conférences données par Laurent Schwartz à l'Université de Montréal au cours du printemps et de l'été 1982. Je suis très reconnaissant d'avoir pu collaborer à ce travail avec le Professeur Schwartz. J'ai utilisé l'expression "il est basé sur" plutôt que "il consigne", du fait que ces notes prennent en compte non seulement la présentation orale du Professeur Schwartz mais aussi le fruit de nombreuses conversations en dehors des leçons formelles, et d'une correspondance sur des sujets qui m'intéressaient, durant la période séparant la série des conférences de la publication. En conséquence, le style est quelque peu inégal, *certaines sections étant bien plus détaillées que d'autres. J'espère que ceci ne m'a pas trop éloigné de l'esprit de la présentation initiale du Professeur Schwartz.*

Je vais maintenant donner un rapide sommaire du contenu de ce livre: dans le premier chapitre, on introduit les principes de base de la théorie générale des processus stochastiques dont nous avons besoin; la section concernant les quasimartingales est particulièrement détaillée. Au deuxième chapitre, la classe des semi-martingales (réelles) est caractérisée comme étant celle des intégrateurs stochastiques "raisonnables" les plus généraux. Au troisième chapitre, on s'intéresse brièvement aux différents modes de convergence des suites de semi-martingales et à leur relation avec l'interprétation des semi-martingales comme intégrateurs; on y introduit les "crochets droits" ("square brackets"*). Au quatrième chapitre, on rappelle la théorie de l'intégration à valeurs vectorielles (non nécessairement Banach) et on interprète les résultats pour* $L^0(\Omega,\mathcal{O},\mathbb{P})$ *qui sont associés à l'intégration stochastique. Les notions de mesure formelle et semi-martingale formelle y sont introduites; elles sont pratiques et très importantes, ainsi que le lecteur pourra le découvrir lors de l'intégration sur les cartes d'une variété. La notion d'équivalence de deux processus sur un sous-ensemble de* $\mathbb{R}_+\times\Omega$ *est traitée au chapitre cinq,* *l'équivalence implique la coïncidence des intégrales stochastiques sur ce sous-ensemble. Cette notion et les résultats la concernant s'avèreront utiles dans divers calculs sur les cartes locales. Le sixième chapitre est consacré à la célèbre formule d'Itô, un théorème fondamental du calcul stochastique, qui n'aurait nécessité aucun commentaire supplémentaire, si ce n'est que son contenu géométrique semble ne pas avoir été souligné jusqu'à ce que Schwartz se rende compte de sa relation heuristique avec la géométrie différentielle du second ordre. Cette relation constitue la base du point de vue adopté pour développer le calcul stochastique des semi-martingales à valeurs dans une variété traité au chapitre huit. Le chapitre sept contient la définition et les propriétés de base d'une semi-martingale à valeurs dans une variété. On y expose aussi le principe de localisation; rapidement: il nous indique comment reconnaître une semi-martingale obtenue par le collage de morceaux de semi-martingales connues. Dans l'appendice, une extension de la théorie de l'intégration stochastique est étudiée; elle nous permettra en partilier d'intégrer par rapport à ces morceaux. Le chapitre neuf est de teneur géométrique et la notion de représentation tangentielle qui y est introduite constitue la base d'une définition globale et intrinsèque d'une équation différentielle stochastique sur une variété. Celle-ci est donnée au chapitre dix, ainsi que les théorèmes de base d'existence et d'unicité, et le comportement temporel asymptotique de leur solution y est étudié. On applique ceci dans le dernier chapitre au problème géométrique du relèvement d'une semi-martingale par une connexion. Un grand nombre d'outils généraux de géométrie différentielle élémentaire (du premier et second ordres) ont été inclus dans les chapitres huit et onze afin qu'autant que possible l'exposé se suffise à lui-même.*

Finalement, un mot au sujet des références s'impose. Il a été décidé que leur liste serait extrêmement courte mais suffisante dans la mesure où, si un résultat ne se trouvait pas dans l'un des livres ou des articles de notre liste, il serait cité dans l'une de leurs bibliographies. Divers auteurs sont mentionnés dans l'exposé; ils ont simplement été pris au hasard dans la présentation du Professeur Schwartz et leur liste ne constitue en aucune façon un survol historique du sujet.

Ian Iscoe

(Traduit par C. Léonard)

INTRODUCTION

This monograph is an exposition of the theory of semi-martingales and their associated stochastic calculus in finite dimensional real vector spaces and on manifolds, based on two series of lectures given by Laurent Schwartz at the Université de Montréal in the spring and late summer of 1982. I am very grateful for having had the opportunity of collaborating with Dr. Schwartz in this work.

I have used the term "based on" rather than "record of" since these notes include not only an account of Doctor Schwartz's oral presentation but also the fruits of the many conversations we shared outside of the formal lectures; as well as written correspondence, on matters which interested me, during the period following the lectures and prior to publication. As a result, there is some degree of unevenness of style, some sections being much more detailed than others.

I hope this has not detracted too much from the flavour of Doctor Schwartz's original presentation.

Turning to matters mathematical, I will give a brief synopsis of the actual contents. The first chapter is of a preparatory nature, introducing the basic concepts needed from the general theory of stochastic processes; the section on quasimartingales is quite detailed. The second chapter is concerned with the characterization of the class of (real) semimartingales as the most general "reasonable" stochastic integrators. The third chapter is a brief look at the various modes of convergence of sequences of semimartingales, and their relation to the interpretation of a (real) semimartingale as an integrator; also the "square brackets" are introduced. In the fourth chapter we review the theory of (not necessarily Banach) vector-valued integration and interpret the results for $L^0(\Omega,\mathcal{O},\mathbb{P})$, which are associated with stochastic integration. Also the notions of formal measure and formal semimartingale are introduced; they are convenient and, as the reader will discover when integrating in a chart on a manifold, very important. Chapter five is concerned with a notion of equivalence of two processes on a subset of $\bar{\mathbb{R}}_+\times\Omega$, with the equivalence implying coincidence of stochastic integrals on the subset. This notion and the results given will also prove useful in various chart-calculations. The sixth chapter deals with the celebrated Itô formula, a Fundamental Theorem of Stochastic Calculus, which would need no further comment, except that its geometric content seemed to go unnoticed until Schwartz recognized its heuristic connection with second order differential geometry. This connection forms the basis of the viewpoint taken in developing the stochastic calculus of semimartingales with values in a manifold, which is covered in chapter eight. In chapter seven the definition and basic properties of a semimartingale with values in a manifold are given. Also covered there is the Localization Principle. Loosely speaking, it tells how to recognize a semimartingale which is defined by gluing together pieces of known semimartingales. In the appendix, an extension of the theory of stochastic integration is discussed which, in particular, allows us to integrate with respect to these "pieces". Chapter nine is geometrical in flavour and the notion of tangential representation introduced there forms the basis of a global, intrinsic definition of a stochastic differential equation on a manifold, given in chapter ten along with the basic existence and uniqueness theorems, and asymptotic behaviour in time. These are applied to the geometrical problem of lifting a semimartingale with respect to a connection, which is considered in the last chapter. Considerable background material on elementary differential geometry (of first and second orders) has been included in chapters eight and eleven in an effort to keep the exposition as selfcontained as possible.

Finally, a word about the references is in order. It was mutually decided that the list be extremely short but adequate in the sense that if a result could not be found in the books or articles of our list, then it would certainly be found in one of their bibliographies. Various names are mentioned in connection with various results in the exposition. They are merely random quotes from Doctor Schwartz's presentation, and in no way represent any attempt at a historical survey of the contributors to this field.

Ian Iscoe

CHAPTER 1

BACKGROUND FROM THE GENERAL THEORY OF PROCESSES

1. PROCESSES AND STOPPING TIMES

The underlying setting throughout these notes is a probability triple $(\Omega,\mathcal{O},\mathbb{P})$ and a *filtration* $\mathcal{T} = (\mathcal{T}_t)_{t\in\bar{\mathbb{R}}_+}$ (where $\bar{\mathbb{R}}_+ = [0,+\infty])$ of σ-algebras satisfying the following "usual hypotheses":

(0) each $\mathcal{T}_t$ is $\mathbb{P}$-measurable

(1) each $\mathcal{T}_t$ is complete, i.e. contains the $\mathbb{P}$-negligible sets of $\mathcal{O}$

(2) for $s \leq t$: $\mathcal{T}_s \subset \mathcal{T}_t$

(3) $\mathcal{T}$ is right continuous: $\bigcap_{s>t} \mathcal{T}_s = \mathcal{T}_t$, for $t < +\infty$.

Remark. The reason for using $\bar{\mathbb{R}}_+$ as opposed to $\mathbb{R}_+=[0,+\infty[$ as an index set is that the former is compact while the latter is not. All that will be done in this context can equally well be carried out for the index sets (intervals) $[0,1]$, $[12,17]$, etc.

A subset of $\bar{\mathbb{R}}_+ \times \Omega$ is said to be $\mathbb{P}$-*negligible* if its projection onto Ω is $\mathbb{P}$-negligible. Given a σ-algebra $\mathcal{A}$ and an $\mathcal{A}$-measurable function X into some measurable target space, we will abbreviate the statement X is $\mathcal{A}$-measurable through the notation $X \in \mathcal{A}$. The completion of $\mathcal{A}$ with respect to some measure μ will be denoted by $\hat{\mathcal{A}}^\mu$ or simply $\hat{\mathcal{A}}$ if μ is understood. If X is real-valued and integrable, its conditional expectation on $\mathcal{A}$ will be denoted by $X/\mathcal{A}$.

By a *process* we shall understand a map $X:\bar{\mathbb{R}}_+ \times \Omega \to E$, a measurable space, which is $\mathcal{T}$-*adapted*: the section $X_t:\omega \mapsto X(t,\omega)$ is $\mathcal{T}_t$-measurable for each $t \in \bar{\mathbb{R}}_+$. A process Y is said to be a *version* of a process X if $\forall t \in \bar{\mathbb{R}}_+, \{\omega \in \Omega : Y(t,\omega) = X(t,\omega)\}$ has probability one. In case E carries a topology and has the Borel σ-algebra $\mathcal{B}$ we will usually consider processes which have some regularity in time. A process X is said to be *cadlag* (from the French: continu à droite et pourvu de limites à gauche) if the sections (*trajectories* or *sample paths*) $X(\omega):t \mapsto X(t,\omega)$ are $\mathbb{P}$-almost surely right continuous and possess left limits. Similarly a process is said to be *caglad* (again borrowed from French) if $\mathbb{P}$-almost surely it is left-continuous and possesses limits from the right. A process is said to be continuous if it is simultaneously cadlag and caglad.

A *stopping time* is a function $T:\Omega \to \bar{\mathbb{R}}_+$ such that for each $t \in \bar{\mathbb{R}}_+$, $\{T \le t\} \in \mathcal{T}_t$. Given stopping times S, T we define the four types of *stochastic intervals:*

$$[S,T] = \{(t,\omega) \in \bar{\mathbb{R}}_+ \times \Omega \colon S(\omega) \le t \le T(\omega)\},$$

$$]S,T] = \{(t,\omega) \in \bar{\mathbb{R}}_+ \times \Omega \colon S(\omega) < t \le T(\omega)\},$$

etc.

A subset $A \subset \bar{\mathbb{R}}_+ \times \Omega$ is said to possess some topological property if each of its sections $A(\omega) := \{t \in \bar{\mathbb{R}}_+ : (t,\omega) \in A\}$ does. Similarly other notions from topology may be transferred from $\bar{\mathbb{R}}_+$ to $\bar{\mathbb{R}}_+ \times \Omega$. In particular the interior of $A \subset \bar{\mathbb{R}}_+ \times \Omega$ will be denoted by A°. Thus $[S,T]$ is closed and if $S \le 1$, $]S,1]^\circ =]S,1[$ but $[0,T[^\circ = [0,T[$ and $[0,+\infty]^\circ = [0,+\infty]$. Much of the theory developed here on $[0,+\infty] \times \Omega$ can be done on $[S,T]$ as well. A function $T:\Omega \to \bar{\mathbb{R}}_+$ is a stopping time iff the indicator of its closed epigraph, $1_{[T,+\infty]}$, is an $\bar{\mathbb{R}}_+$-valued process ($\bar{\mathbb{R}}_+$ always carries the Borel σ-algebra $\mathcal{B}$).

As an example of a stopping time, consider an $\mathbb{R}^d$-valued Brownian motion B with $B_0 = 0$ and define $T(\omega) = \inf\{t > 0\colon B(t,\omega) \in S^{d-1}\}$ where S^{d-1} is the unit sphere in $\mathbb{R}^d$. Then T is a stopping time. Also the minimum and maximum of two stopping times are also stopping times. More generally, the limit and limsup of a sequence of stopping times is again a stopping time.

In the example above $T < +\infty$ almost surely but for a set more general than S^{d-1} this may not be the case. As we have defined T it would then take the value $+\infty$ on some portion of Ω. If B is replaced by a process X (which has a value at $t = +\infty$) this could be inappropriate. It is convenient (in fact necessary for the theory being presented) to adjoin an element $\overline{+\infty}$ to $\bar{\mathbb{R}}_+$ and admit stopping times $T:\Omega \to \bar{\mathbb{R}}_+ \cup \{\overline{+\infty}\}$ with the convention that $\mathcal{T}_{\overline{+\infty}} = \mathcal{T}_{+\infty}$ and $X_{\overline{+\infty}} = X_{+\infty}$. Intuitively the value $T(\omega) = \overline{+\infty}$ corresponds to some "event" which never occurs for the sample ω. By convention $t < \overline{+\infty}$ for all $t \in \bar{\mathbb{R}}_+$.

Associated with a stopping time T is the *stopped σ-algebra* $\mathcal{T}_T$ defined to be the collection of subsets $\{A \subset \Omega:$ $A \cap \{T \leq t\} \in \mathcal{T}_t$, for all $t \in \bar{\mathbb{R}}_+\}$. Clearly $T \in \mathcal{T}_T$. Given a process X and a stopping time T we can form the random variable X_T and the *stopped process* X^T defined respectively by $X_T(\omega) = X_{T(\omega)}(\omega)$ and $X^T(t,\omega) = X(T(\omega) \wedge t,\omega)$ ($a \wedge b$, $a \vee b$ denote the minimum and maximum of two real numbers a,b). If X is cadlag then it can be shown that $X_T \in \mathcal{T}_T$, $X_{T-} \equiv X_{+\infty}$ on $\{T = \overline{+\infty}\}$.

In order to avoid confusion, indexing of a family of processes will be notated in parentheses as superscripts or subscripts, the choice depending on the availability of space. As an illustration, $X_T^{(n)} = [X^{(n)}]_T$ is the process $X^{(n)}$ evaluated at the random time T, whereas $X_{(n)}^T = [X_{(n)}]^T$ is the process $X^{(n)}$ stopped at time T, which is again a process.

An increasing sequence $(T_n)_{n\in\mathbb{N}}$ of stopping times is said to converge *stationarily* to T (necessarily a stopping time) if for $\mathbb{P}$-almost every $\omega \in \Omega$ there exists an $n_\omega \in \mathbb{N}$ such that $T_n(\omega) = T(\omega)$. We write in this situation: $T_n \uparrow\uparrow T$.

2. MARTINGALES AND LOCAL MARTINGALES

We now come to the notion of a martingale, an important building block of the processes to be studied here. A process $M:\bar{\mathbb{R}}_+ \times \Omega \to E$, a finite dimensional real vector space, is called an E-$\mathcal{T}$-$\mathbb{P}$-*martingale*, or briefly a *martingale* if it satisfies:

(1) M_t is $\mathbb{P}$-integrable for each $t \in \bar{\mathbb{R}}_+$

(2) for $s \leq t$, $M_t/\mathcal{T}_s = M_s : \forall A \in \mathcal{T}_s$, $\int_A M_t dP = \int_A M_s dP$.

We have the following useful regularity theorem for martingales.

<u>Theorem.</u> Every martingale admits a cadlag version.

We shall usually assume without explicit mention that we are dealing with such a version if necessary.

More generally we have the notion of a local martingale: a process M is called a *local martingale* if there exists a sequence $(T_n)_{n\in N}$ of stopping times, $T_n \uparrow\uparrow +\infty$ (or $\overline{+\infty}$ if appropriate), such that for each $n \in N$, $M^{T_n} - M_0$ is a martingale. We have normalized the stopped local martingale at time t=0 to avoid integrability problems with M_0: $M_0^{T_n} = M_0$ for all n.

In general we will be taking the attitude of trying to avoid unpleasantries at times $t=0,+\infty$ as much as possible (see for instance the section on the predictable σ-algebra). We can assume without loss of generality, as with martingales, that our local martingales are cadlag.

Examples of local martingales

1. Every martingale is a local martingale (take $T_n = +\infty$ for all $n \in \mathbb{N}$).

2. If M and N are two local martingales then so is M+N. To see this we must appeal to a theorem of Doob which states that a stopped martingale is again a martingale. Now if $S_n, T_n \uparrow\uparrow +\infty$ such that $M^{S_n}-M_0$ and $N^{T_n}-N_0$ are both martingales for each n, then

$$(M+N)^{S_n \wedge T_n}-(M_0+N_0) = (M^{S_n}-M_0)^{T_n}+(N^{T_n}-N_0)^{S_n}$$

and Doob's theorem applied to each summand yields the desired result.

3. A very simple example of a local martingale, which is not a martingale, is the following one given in discrete time. It is no problem at all to fill in the ingredients, in this and the next example, in a right continuous and complete manner (but as the essential features are already exhibited in the discrete setting we shall not do so): simply complete $\mathcal{T}_n$ to $\hat{\mathcal{T}}_n$ and set $\mathcal{T}_t = \hat{\mathcal{T}}_{[t]}$ and $M_t = M_{[t]}$ where [t] denotes the

integer part of t. We take $\Omega =]0,1]$, $\mathcal{O} = \mathcal{B}$, and $\mathbb{P}$ = Lebesgue measure. We set

$$\mathcal{T}_0 = \sigma\{]\tfrac{1}{n+1}, \tfrac{1}{n}], \quad n=1,2,\ldots\}$$
$$(\mathcal{T}_n = \mathcal{T}_0)$$
$$\mathcal{T}_{+\infty} = \mathcal{B}$$

and define

$$M_0 \equiv 0$$
$$(M_n \equiv M_0)$$

$M_{+\infty} \equiv$ any Borel measurable, non-integrable function which is, however, integrable on each subinterval $]\frac{1}{n+1}, \frac{1}{n}]$, with integral value 0.

(In this example we have only two times: $0,+\infty$; one can take $\mathcal{T}_n = \mathcal{T}_0$, $M_n \equiv M_0$.)

As such M is clearly adapted, and defining stopping times $(T_n)_{n\in\mathbb{N}}$ by

$$T_n = \begin{cases} 0 & \text{on }]0, \frac{1}{n}] \\ \overline{+\infty} & \text{elsewhere} \end{cases}$$

renders

$$M_k^{T_n} = \begin{cases} 0 & \text{on }]0, \frac{1}{n}] \\ M_k & \text{elsewhere} \end{cases} \qquad (k=0,+\infty)$$

a martingale. Indeed M^{T_n} is clearly integrable, adapted, and

$$\int_{]\frac{1}{m+1}, \frac{1}{m}]} M_{+\infty}^{T_n} \, dP = 0 = \int_{]\frac{1}{m+1}, \frac{1}{m}]} M_0^{T_n} \, dP .$$

Since $M_{+\infty}$ is not integrable, M is not a martingale.

4. In this example we shall exhibit a local martingale which is again not a martingale but is however integrable, moreover bounded, at each instant. We take $(\Omega,\mathcal{O},\mathbb{P})$ as above and set

$$\mathcal{T}_n=\sigma\{]k\cdot 2^{-n},(k+1)\cdot 2^{-n}],\ k=0,1,\ldots,2^n-1\},\quad M_n=2^n\cdot 1_{]0,2^{-n}]},\quad n\in\mathbb{N}$$

$$\mathcal{T}_{+\infty}=\mathcal{B},\qquad M_{+\infty}=0.$$

Then M is clearly adapted and integrable (in fact bounded at each instant) but is not a martingale since $\mathbb{E}M_{+\infty}=0\neq 1=\mathbb{E}M_n$ for each $n\in\mathbb{N}$.

If we define stopping times $(T_n)_{n\in\mathbb{N}}$ by

$$T_n=\begin{cases} n & \text{on }]0,2^{-n}] \\ \overline{+\infty} & \text{elsewhere}\end{cases}$$

then

$$M_k^{T_n}=\begin{cases} M_k & \text{if } k\leq n \\ M_n & \text{if } k>n\end{cases}$$

and is clearly adapted and bounded, hence integrable. Finally, M^{T_n} is a martingale:

$$\int_{]k2^{-n},(k+1)\cdot 2^{-n}]} M_{n+1}\,dP=\int_{]2k\cdot 2^{-(n+1)},(2k+1)\cdot 2^{-(n+1)}]} M_{n+1}\,dP$$

$$+\int_{](2k+1)\cdot 2^{-(n+1)},(2k+2)\cdot 2^{-(n+1)}} M_{n+1}\,dP=\begin{cases}0+0, & \text{if } k\neq 0\\ 1+0, & \text{if } k=0\end{cases}$$

and

$$\int_{]k2^{-n},(k+1)\cdot 2^{-n}]} M_n\,dP=\begin{cases}0, & \text{if } k\neq 0\\ 1, & \text{if } k=0\end{cases}$$

The following picture summarizes this calculation:

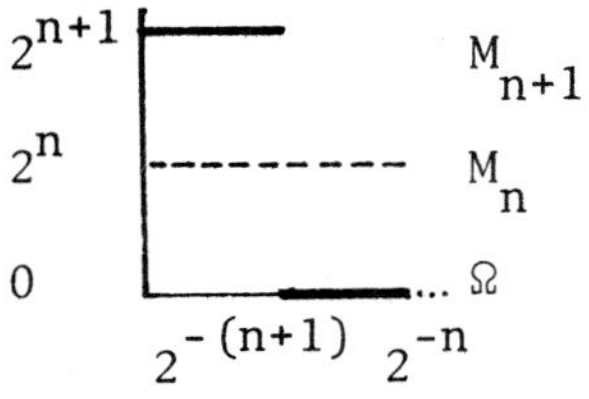

(M_{n+1} is solid, M_n is dashed).

There is a certain criterion due to Doob which singles out the class of martingales from the class of local martingales.

Theorem. A local martingale M is a martingale iff M is of *class* D: $\{M_T,\ T \text{ a stopping time}\}$ is uniformly integrable i.e. if $(A_n)_{n\in\mathbb{N}}$ are $\mathbb{P}$-measurable and $\mathbb{P}(A_n) \to 0$ as $n \to +\infty$ then $\int_{A_n} M_T\, dP \to 0$ uniformly in T as $n \to +\infty$.

Proof. Assume M is a local martingale of class D, with $M_0 = 0$ for simplicity. In particular M_t is integrable and if $A \in \mathcal{T}_s$ with $s \le t$:

$$\int_A M_{T_n \wedge s}\, dP = \int_A M_{T_n \wedge t}\, dP$$

where $(T_n)_{n\in\mathbb{N}}$ is a localizing sequence for M. Now $M_{T_n\wedge s} \to M_s$ and $M_{T_n\wedge t} \to M_t$ pointwise as $n \to +\infty$ with $(M_{T_n\wedge s})_{n\in\mathbb{N}}$ and $(M_{T_n\wedge t})_{n\in\mathbb{N}}$ being uniformly integrable. By the generalized Lebesgue dominated convergence theorem we can conclude that

$$\int_A M_s\, dP = \int_A M_t\, dP$$

i.e. M is a martingale.

Conversely, if M is a martingale it is well-known that all its conditional expectations are uniformly integrable; and $M_T = M_{+\infty}/\mathcal{T}_T$. □

It is interesting to note that the procedure of localizing to obtain a martingale does not yield anything new if applied twice — if a sequence $(T_n)_{n\in\mathbb{N}}$ of stopping times, $T_n \uparrow\uparrow +\infty$, is such that M^{T_n} is a local martingale for each $n \in \mathbb{N}$, then M itself was already a local martingale. To see this we first introduce the following terminology. A stopping time T is said to *reduce* a process M with $M_0 = 0$, if M^T is a martingale. It follows easily from the theorem of Doob stated in local martingale example (2) that the minimum of two reducing stopping times is again reducing: $M^{S\wedge T} = (M^S)^T$; so in fact only one of them need be reducing. That the maximum of two reducing stopping times is reducing, is less evident and we verify it in the following lemma.

Lemma. If S,T reduce M then $S\vee T$ reduces M.

Proof. It suffices, by the previous theorem, to show that the family $\{M_U^{S\vee T}$, U a stopping time$\}$ is uniformly integrable. On $\{S \le T\}$, $M_U^{S\vee T} = M_U^T$ and on $\{S > T\}$, $M_U^{S\vee T} = M_U^S$; so we are done. □

Returning to the main point, we are given a sequence $(T_{n,m})_{m\in\mathbb{N}}$, $T_{n,m}\uparrow\uparrow +\infty$, such that $M^{T_n\wedge T_{n,m}} = (M^{T_n})^{T_{n,m}}$ is a martingale for each $n \in \mathbb{N}$. Reorder $(T_n \wedge T_{n,m})_{(n,m)\in\mathbb{N}^2}$ into a sequence $(S_j)_{j\in\mathbb{N}}$ and define $\tilde{T}_k = \max_{1\le j\le k} S_j$. Each $\tilde{T}$ is easily seen to be a stopping time and reduces M by virtue of the lemma. Since both $(T_n)_{n\in\mathbb{N}}$ and $(T_{n,m})_{(n,m)\in\mathbb{N}^2}$ are stationary, $T_n \wedge T_{n,m} = +\infty$ for $\mathbb{P}$-almost every $\omega \in \Omega$ and large n and m, i.e. $S_j(\omega) = +\infty$ for some j_ω, which yields the stationarity of $(\tilde{T}_k)_{k\in\mathbb{N}}$.

3. SEMIMARTINGALES

A very general class of processes, which is at the same time rich in structure, is that of semimartingales. A cadlag process $X:\bar{\mathbb{R}}_+\times\Omega \to E$, E a finite dimensional real vector space, is said to be an E-*semimartingale* if it admits a decomposition X = V+M with V cadlag and of *finite variation* ($\int_{[0,+\infty]} |dV_s(\omega)| < +\infty$ for $\mathbb{P}$-almost all ω) and M a local martingale. (Unless specified to the contrary, all processes with finite variation will be assumed cadlag.) Note that, because of the stationarity clause in the notion of "local", the concept of locally finite variation coincides with that of finite variation. Also the decomposition in the definition of a semimartingale is not unique; trivially so since one can always trade a constant between V and M, but moreover there exist discontinuous martingales of finite variation which then decompose: M = 0+M = M+0.

One does have a uniqueness criterion for a suitable decomposition of a continuous semimartingale, which we state as a theorem.

<u>Theorem</u>. A continuous semimartingale X admits a unique (up to an additive constant) decomposition X = V+M into a continuous process V of finite variation and a continuous local martingale.

An ingredient of the proof of this theorem is the fact that a continuous local martingale of finite variation is a constant process, from which the uniqueness follows.

Returning to the general cadlag case, it is fruitful to think of the difference between a semimartingale and a (local) martingale as being analogous to that of a manifold and a Euclidean space. The decomposition X = V+M corresponds to a decomposition of a manifold into charts and so it should not be surprising that certain decompositions are more suitable for a given calculation than others.

Concerning the evolutionary aspect of a semimartingale X, the decomposition X = V+M represents X as a sum of a slowly varying "drift" V and a (usually) rapidly oscillating "fluctuation" M.

The richness which was alluded to, at the beginning of this section, is exemplified by the following stability properties of the class of semimartingales. Let X be an

E-$\mathcal{T}$-semimartingale, then:

1. If $\Phi:E \to F$ is C^2 then $\Phi(X)$ is an F-semimartingale.
2. (*Girsanov property*) If $\mathbb{Q} \approx \mathbb{P}$ then X remains a semimartingale with respect to Q, i.e. $X = V'+M'$ with V' of finite variation $\mathbb{Q}$-almost surely and M' a $\mathbb{Q}$-local martingale.
3. If $\mathbb{P} = \int_{\mathcal{X}} \mathbb{P}_x \mu(dx)$ and X is a $\mathbb{P}_x$ semimartingale for each x, then X is also a $\mathbb{P}$-semimartingale.
4. If $\mathcal{S} \subset \mathcal{T}$ and X is $\mathcal{S}$-adapted then X is an $\mathcal{S}$-semimartingale.

Proofs of properties 1 and 4 will be given further on in these notes.

The class of semimartingales although rich and wide is not however all-encompassing. It is known for instance that $\sqrt{|B|}$ (B - a Brownian motion on [0,1], say) is not a semimartingale.

4. OPTIONAL AND PREDICTABLE σ-ALGEBRAS

In order that the role of a semimartingale X, as a stochastic integrator, may be discussed, it is necessary to consider X on $\bar{\mathbb{R}}_+\times\Omega$ (or a subset thereof) and classes of integrands measurable with respect to certain σ-algebras on $\bar{\mathbb{R}}_+\times\Omega$. Two such σ-algebras, the optional and predictable, carry considerable importance.

The *optional σ-algebra*, denoted by *Opt*, (resp. *Pre* = *predictable σ-algebra*) is defined to be that generated by the closed (resp. open) epigraphs of the $\bar{\mathbb{R}}_+ \cup \{\overline{+\infty}\}$-valued $\mathcal{T}$-stopping times, with the conventions that $[\overline{+\infty}, +\infty] =]\overline{+\infty}, +\infty] = \phi$, and that $\{0\}\times\mathcal{T}_0$ is also considered part of Pre.

The important relation Pre ⊂ Opt can be seen as follows. We first note that for each $t \in \bar{\mathbb{R}}_+$, $\{t\}\times\mathcal{T}_t \subset$ Opt. Indeed if $t \in \mathbb{R}_+$ and $A \in \mathcal{T}_t$ we can define the sequence T^n_A of stopping times by

$$T^n_A(\omega) = \begin{cases} t, & \omega \in A \\ t + \frac{1}{n}, & \omega \notin A \end{cases}$$

and $\{t\}\times A = \bigcap_{n\in N} [T^n_A, t+\frac{1}{n}[$. If $t = +\infty$ and $A \in \mathcal{T}_{+\infty}$ then we use the stopping time

$$T_A(\omega) = \begin{cases} +\infty, & \omega \in A \\ \overline{+\infty}, & \omega \notin A \end{cases}$$

to represent $\{+\infty\}\times A = [T_A, +\infty]$. (It is here where the admission of $\bar{\mathbb{R}}_+ \cup \{\overline{+\infty}\}$-valued stopping times is essential. If the value $\overline{+\infty}$ were not allowed and $\mathcal{T}_{+\infty} \neq \{\phi, \Omega\}$ then we could not have $\{+\infty\}\times\mathcal{T}_{+\infty} \subset$ Opt, since if $T \leq +\infty$ then $[T, +\infty] \supset \{+\infty\}\times\Omega$; thus for $A \in$ Opt, $A \cap \{+\infty\}\times\Omega$ would always be ϕ or $\{+\infty\}\times\Omega$, with no intermediate possibilities.) Therefore in particular $\{0\}\times\mathcal{T}_0 \subset$ Opt, and if T is a stopping time then $]T, +\infty] = (\bigcup_{n\in N} [T+\frac{1}{n}, +\infty])\setminus(\{+\infty\}\times\{T=+\infty\})$; $T+\frac{1}{n}$ is a stopping time and $\{T = +\infty\} \in \mathcal{T}_{+\infty}$ so that $\{+\infty\}\times\{T=+\infty\} \in \mathrm{Opt}$, $]T,+\infty] \in \mathrm{Opt}$, and $\mathrm{Pre} \subset \mathrm{Opt}$ has been established.

Alternate characterizations of these σ-algebras can be given. For instance Pre is also generated by the family of caglad processes. One inclusion is established as follows. If T is a stopping time then $1_{]T,+\infty]}$ is a caglad process and $]T,+\infty] = \{1_{]T,+\infty]}=1\}$. Also if $A \in \mathcal{T}_0$ then $1_{\{0\}\times A}$ is a caglad process and $\{0\}\times A = \{1_{\{0\}\times A}=1\}$. For the other inclusion one need only consider the predictable approximation, $X^{(\varepsilon)}$, of a caglad process X:

$$X^{(\varepsilon)} = \sum_{n=0}^{+\infty} X_{t_n} 1_{]t_n,t_{n+1}]} + X_0 1_{\{0\}\times\Omega} + X_{+\infty} 1_{\{+\infty\}\times\Omega}, \text{ where } t_n = n\varepsilon.$$

As $X_{t_n} \in \mathcal{T}_{t_n}$, X_{t_n} can be approximated by a simple function, say $\sum_{k=1}^{K_n} a_{nk} 1_{A_{nk}}$ with $A_{nk} \in \mathcal{T}_{t_n}$. It only remains to observe that $1_{]t_n,t_{n+1}]} 1_{A_{nk}} =]S,T]$ where $S = t_n$ and $T = t_n + (t_{n+1}-t_n)\cdot 1_{A_{nk}}$.

It is also the case that Pre is generated by the family of continuous processes. Denoting the σ-algebra generated by the family of continuous processes by $\mathcal{C}$, the results of the previous paragraph imply that $\mathcal{C} \subset \mathrm{Pre}$. To obtain the other inclusion, we observe that if T is a stopping time and f is defined by $f(t,\omega) = \max(0,t-T(\omega))$ with the convention that $f(\cdot,\omega) = 0$ if $T(\omega) = +\infty$ or $\overline{+\infty}$, then f is a continuous process and $]T,+\infty] = \{f > 0\}$. Also if $A \in \mathcal{T}_0$ and we define

$$g(t,\omega) = \begin{cases} t\wedge 1, & \omega \in A \\ 1, & \omega \notin A \end{cases}$$

then g is a continuous process and $\{0\}\times A = \{g=0\}$.

Also the optional σ-algebra is generated by the family of cadlag processes. Again one direction is easy: if T is a stopping time then $1_{[T,+\infty]}$ is a cadlag process and $[T,+\infty] = \{1_{[T,+\infty]} = 1\}$. The other inclusion requires some work of which we only give an indication. Given $\varepsilon > 0$, define a sequence of stopping times $(T_n^\varepsilon)_{n\in\mathbb{N}}$ by $T_0^\varepsilon = 0$ and $T_{n+1}^\varepsilon = \inf\{t > T_n^\varepsilon: |X_t - X_{T_n^\varepsilon}| > \varepsilon\}$ (that each T_n^ε is a stopping time may be established by induction). Also define an ε-approximation, $X^{(\varepsilon)}$ of X by $X^{(\varepsilon)} = \sum_{n=0}^{+\infty} X_{T_n^\varepsilon} \cdot 1_{[T_n^\varepsilon, T_{n+1}^\varepsilon[}$. It can be shown that $X^{(\varepsilon)}$ is adapted and that each $X_{T_n^\varepsilon} \cdot 1_{[T_n^\varepsilon, T_{n+1}^\varepsilon[}$ is optionally measurable.

We conclude this section with a brief discussion of predictable stopping times. A stopping time T is said to be *announcible* if there exists an (*announcing*) sequence $(T_n)_{n\in\mathbb{N}}$ of stopping times such that $T_n\uparrow$, $T_n < T$ on $\{T > 0\}$, $T_n \uparrow T$ on $\{T < \overline{+\infty}\}$, and $T_n \uparrow\uparrow +\infty$ on $\{T=\overline{+\infty}\}$. More generally we can speak of T being announcible on some $\mathbb{P}$-measurable subset of by restricting the requirements of the definition to hold only on the given subset. T is called (totally) inaccessible if whenever $T_n \uparrow T$ a.e. then the convergence is stationary a.e.

Examples.

1. Let K be a compact subset of $\mathbb{R}^d$ and X an $\mathbb{R}^d$-valued continuous process. Define $T = \inf\{t>0: X_t \in K\}$; then T is announcible and is announced, for example, by $(T_n)_{n\in\mathbb{N}}$ where $T_n = \inf\{t > 0: X_t \in K_n\}$ and where $(K_n)_{n\in\mathbb{N}}$ is a decreasing sequence of compact sets containing K in their interior and whose intersection is K.

2. (Due to Dellacherie) Let $\Omega = \mathbb{R}_+$, $\mathcal{F} = \mathcal{B}$, and $\mathbb{P}$ equivalent to Lebesgue measure. Consider the stopping time T = id with respect to the minimal filtration $\mathcal{T}_t = \mathcal{B}\cap[0,t]\vee\{]t,+\infty]\}$. If S is a stopping time with $S < T$ on $\{T > 0\}$ then $\{S=S(s)\} \in \mathcal{T}_{S(s)}$. Therefore $\{S = S(s)\}$ either contains $]S(s),+\infty[$ or is disjoint from it. Since every positive s belongs to both we conclude that for each $s > 0$, S is the constant S(s) on $]S(s),+\infty[$ i.e. $S \equiv 0$. Therefore T is totally inaccessible.

A stopping time T is said to be *predictable* if its graph $[T] \in$ Pre, or equivalently $[T,+\infty] =]T,+\infty]\cup[T] \in$ Pre. If T is announcible then T is predictable since $[T,+\infty] = \bigcap_{n\in\mathbb{N}}]T_n,+\infty]\cup(\{0\}\times\{T=0\})$. It is a theorem of Dellacherie that a converse is true provided that we assume, as we do here, that the underlying filtration $(\mathcal{T}_t)_{t\in\bar{\mathbb{R}}_+}$ is $\mathbb{P}$-complete (counter-examples exist in the absence of this hypothesis): if T is predictable then T is $\mathbb{P}$-announcible i.e. $\exists (T_n)_{n\in\mathbb{N}}$, stopping times, such that $T_n\uparrow$, $\lim_{n\to\infty} T_n \leq T$ and $= T$ $\mathbb{P}$-a.e. with $T_n < T$ on $\{T > 0\}$ $\mathbb{P}$-a.e.

However, even without the completeness assumption, we can show that the σ-algebra $\mathcal{P}$ generated by the closed epigraphs of announcible stopping times coincides with the σ-algebra generated by the closed epigraphs of predictable stopping times; moreover they are both equal to Pre. To see this we first note that if T is a stopping time such that $T \leq +\infty$ and $\tau > 0$, then $T+\tau$ is announcible since it is announced by $(T+\tau-\frac{1}{n})\wedge n$ for $n > \frac{1}{\tau}$ $(T+\tau-\frac{1}{n}$ does not announce $T+\tau$ on $\{T=+\infty\})$. Also one sees easily that $\{0\}\times\mathcal{T}_0 \subset \mathcal{P}$ and $\{+\infty\}\times\mathcal{T}_{+\infty-} \subset \mathcal{P}$. Then for any stopping time T, letting $T' = T\wedge+\infty$: $]T,+\infty] =]T',+\infty] = \bigcup_{n\in N} [T'+\frac{1}{n},+\infty]\setminus(\{+\infty\}\times\{T'=+\infty\}) \in \mathcal{P}$, and we are done.

We point out in closing that if the value $\overline{+\infty}$ lies in the range of T then it is not necessarily true that $T+\tau$ is announcible nor even predictable. For instance if $A \in \mathcal{T}_{+\infty}\setminus\mathcal{T}_{+\infty-}$ and $T_A = \begin{cases} +\infty & \text{on } A \\ \overline{+\infty} & \text{on } \Omega\setminus A \end{cases}$ then T_A is a stopping time but it is not predictable (if S is predictable then $\{S=+\infty\} \in \mathcal{T}_{+\infty-}$); however $T_A+\tau = T_A$. One can prove that $T+\tau$ is predictable (not necessarily announcible) iff $\{T=+\infty\}$ or $\{T=\overline{+\infty}\} \in \mathcal{T}_{+\infty-}$.

5 QUASIMARTINGALES AND OBLIQUE BRACKETS

A process X, right continuous in probability, is said to be a *quasimartingale* if $\sup \mathbb{E} \sum_i |(X_{t_{i+1}} - X_{t_i})/\mathcal{T}_i| < +\infty$ where the supremum is taken over all partitions $\{t_i\}$ of $[0,+\infty]$.

Examples of quasimartingales are furnished by martingales and cadlag *submartingales* - these are $\mathbb{P}$-integrable processes X which satisfy $X_t/\mathcal{T}_s \geq X_s$ for $s \leq t$ (for an example, see example (2) in the section on local martingales). For these two classes the sum in the definition of a quasimartingale telescopes.

If X is also of class D for the discrete stopping times (i.e. those whose range is of finite cardinality), then there exists a cadlag version of X which is a semimartingale admitting a *special decomposition* $X = V+M$, where V is a predictable cadlag process of *integrable variation* ($\mathbb{E} \int_{[0,+\infty]} |dV_s| < +\infty$) and M is a martingale; this decomposition is unique up to an additive constant. For quasimartingales $X = V+M$ of class D, the uniform summability condition in the definition expresses that $\sup \mathbb{E} \sum_i |V_{t_{i+1}} - V_{t_i}| < +\infty$. We will now indicate the main idea of the proof of the existence and uniqueness of this special decomposition.

One can associate with X a real measure ρ_X on Pre by defining firstly $\rho_X(]S,T]) := \mathbb{E}(X_T - X_S)$ (or $\rho_X]s,t]\times A) :=$

$\mathbb{E}\, 1_A \cdot (X_t - X_s)$, for $A \in \mathcal{T}_s$ and $\rho_X(\{0\} \times A) = 0$ for $A \in \mathcal{T}_0$) and using the hypotheses on X to show that ρ_X extends to Pre. A theorem of C. Doleans-Dade asserts that such a measure ρ_X has a unique representation as the expectation of a Stieltjes integral with respect to a cadlag predictable process V of integrable variation: $\rho_X(H) = \mathbb{E} \int_{]0,+\infty]} H_s dV_s$, for all bounded and predictable processes H. Thus

$$\mathbb{E}[1_A \cdot (X_t - X_s)] = \rho_X(]s,t] \times A) = \mathbb{E}[1_A \cdot \int_{]0,+\infty]} 1_{]s,t]} dV] = \mathbb{E}[1_A \cdot (V_t - V_s)]$$

for $A \in \mathcal{T}_s$, and rearranging we obtain: $\mathbb{E}[1_A \cdot (X_t - V_t)] = \mathbb{E}[1_A \cdot (X_s - V_s)]$ for $A \in \mathcal{T}_s$, i.e. X-V is a martingale, which has a cadlag version.

Concerning the uniqueness of the decomposition, it is equivalent to the constancy of a cadlag predictable martingale of integrable variation. In fact more is true. It is known that a cadlag predictable local martingale is continuous, and also that a continuous local martingale of finite variation is a constant process (as mentioned in the section on semimartingales). Thus the uniqueness follows.

If X is a quasimartingale, not necessarily of class D, we can still show that X is at least locally of class D; that X is a semimartingale then follows easily. The subtle point involved in showing that X is locally of class D, is establishing the existence of a cadlag version of X. Towards this end and ultimately the result itself, we prove two lemmas.

Lemma 1. Let X be a quasimartingale with $\mathbb{E}|X_{+\infty}| \leq K$ and:

(QM) $$\sup \mathbb{E}\left(\sum_i |(X_{t_{i+1}} - X_{t_i})/\mathcal{T}_{t_i}|\right) \leq K$$

where the sup is taken over all partitions $\{t_i\}$ of $\bar{\mathbb{R}}_+$. Then for every $t \in \bar{\mathbb{R}}_+$ $\mathbb{E}|X_t| \leq 2K$ and for all $R > 0$

$\mathbb{P}(\sup_{t\in\bar{\mathbb{Q}}_+} |X_t| > R) \leq \frac{2K}{R}$; in particular $(\sup_{t\in\bar{\mathbb{Q}}_+} |X_t|) < +\infty$ $\mathbb{P}$-a.e.

($\bar{\mathbb{Q}}_+ = \mathbb{Q}_+ \cup \{\overline{+\infty}\}$, $\mathbb{Q}_+$ being the non-negative rationals).

Proof. $\mathbb{E}|X_t| = \mathbb{E}|X_t/\mathcal{T}_t| \leq \mathbb{E}(|X_{+\infty}|/\mathcal{T}_t) + \mathbb{E}(|X_{+\infty} - X_t|/\mathcal{T}_t) \leq 2K$. Now if T is a stopping time with finitely many values in its range (briefly T has finite range) then one can verify that the following inequality of type (QM) still holds:

$$\mathbb{E}(|(X_T - X_0)/\mathcal{T}_0| + |(X_{+\infty} - X_T)/\mathcal{T}_T|) \leq K;$$

and so we can derive that $\mathbb{E}|X_T| \leq 2K$ as above.

Let J be a finite subset of $\bar{\mathbb{Q}}_+$ and set $T_J = \inf\{t \in J: |X_t| > R\}$; T_J has a finite range contained in $J \cup \{\overline{+\infty}\}$. Therefore $\mathbb{P}(\sup_{t\in J} |X_t| > R) \leq \mathbb{P}(|X_{T_J}| > R) \leq \frac{2K}{R}$. By taking a sequence $J_n \uparrow \bar{\mathbb{Q}}_+$: $\mathbb{P}(\sup_{t\in\bar{\mathbb{Q}}_+} |X_t| > R) \leq \frac{2K}{R}$, therefore $\sup_{t\in\bar{\mathbb{Q}}_+} |X_t| < +\infty$ $\mathbb{P}$-a.e. □

For technical reasons we will not be able to deal with X stopped directly; we will have to work firstly with certain "modifications". Towards this end we prove the next lemma.

Lemma 2. Let $(Y_{-n})_{n\in\mathbb{N}}$ be a sequence of integrable random variables, $Y_{-n} \in \mathcal{S}_{-n}$, where $(\mathcal{S}_{-n})_{n\in\mathbb{N}}$ is a decreasing sequence of σ-algebras with $\bigcap_{n\in N} \mathcal{S}_{-n} = \mathcal{S}_{-\infty}$. Assume that

$$\mathbb{E} \sum_{k\in\mathbb{N}} |(Y_{-k}-Y_{-(k+1)})/\mathcal{S}_{-(k+1)}| \leq K < +\infty.$$

Then $(Y_{-n})_{n\in\mathbb{N}}$ is convergent in L^1.

Proof. Let $\varepsilon > 0$. For q sufficiently large $\mathbb{E} \sum_{k\geq q} |(Y_{-k}-Y_{-(k+1)})/\mathcal{S}_{-(q+1)}| \leq \varepsilon$. For $n \geq q+1$, one sees easily that $\mathbb{E}|(Y_{-q}-Y_{-n})/\mathcal{S}_{-n}| \leq \varepsilon$. Now $(Y_{-q}/\mathcal{S}_{-n})_{n\in\mathbb{N}}$ is a martingale with decreasing indices; it converges in L^1 to $Y_{-q}/\mathcal{S}_{-\infty}$. Therefore $(Y_{-n}=Y_{-n}/\mathcal{S}_{-n})_{n\in\mathbb{N}}$ is an L^1-Cauchy sequence up to an error of at most ε; ε being arbitrary, $(Y_{-n})_{n\in\mathbb{N}}$ is Cauchy in L^1 and so is convergent in L^1. □

By the proof of Lemma 1 we can apply lemma 2 to the following situation: let X be a quasimartingale and $(T_n)_{n\in\mathbb{N}}$ a sequence of stopping times with finite ranges such that $T_n \downarrow T$; put $Y_n = X_{T_n}$, $\mathcal{S}_{-n} = \mathcal{T}_{T_n}$, $\mathcal{S}_{-\infty} = \mathcal{T}_T$. We conclude that $(X_{T_n})_{n\in\mathbb{N}}$ is convergent in L^1; its limit is not well known. It is rather long and technical to show that this limit is independent of $(T_n)_{n\in\mathbb{N}}$ as long as $T_n \downarrow T$ (for instance, if $T_n \downarrow \tau$, a fixed time, it is not trivial that the limit is actually X_τ); we shall omit the details and assume this result. However if $T_n = t_n$, fixed times, with $t_n \downarrow t$ then since $X_{t_n} \to X_t$ in probability, the mysterious limit in L^1 must also be X_t; a quasimartingale (which is right continuous by our definition) is thus right continuous in L^1.

Given any stopping time T we can now form an integrable random variable from X and T by $L^1\text{-}\lim_{n\to+\infty} X_{T_n}$ where $T_n \downarrow T$ and each T_n has finite range; of course if X has right continuous sample paths then it is just X_T. Applying this to X and $T\wedge t$ we obtain a process $Y_t = L^1\text{-}\lim_{n\to+\infty} X_{T_n\wedge t}$; it is again a quasi-martingale, right continuous in L^1. Now set $T_k = \inf\{t\in\overline{\mathbb{Q}}_+ : |X_t| > k\}$; by lemma 1, $T_k \uparrow\uparrow \overline{+\infty}$ $\mathbb{P}$-a.e. Repeating the construction of this paragraph for each T_k, we obtain a sequence $(Y^{(k)})_{k\in\mathbb{N}}$ of quasimartingales which are right continuous in L^1, such that for each t, $Y_t^{(k)}(\omega) = X_t(\omega)$ $\mathbb{P}$-a.e. for sufficiently large $k = k(\omega)$, and such that for all $t \in \mathbb{Q}_+ : |Y_t^{(k)}| \le k\vee|Y_{+\infty}^{(k)}|$ a.e. . From the L^1 right continuity of $Y^{(k)}$ it follows that for each $t \in \overline{\mathbb{R}}_+$, $|Y_t^{(k)}| \le k\vee|Y_{+\infty}^{(k)}|$ a.e., and so if S is a stopping time with finite range then $|Y_S^{(k)}| \le k\vee|Y_{+\infty}^{(k)}|$ a.e., i.e. $Y^{(k)}$ is of class D with respect to the family of stopping times having finite range. Therefore $Y^{(k)}$ has a cadlag version, which is a semimartingale. Setting $\tilde{X}(t,\omega) = \tilde{Y}^{(k)}(t,\omega)$, where $k = k(\omega)$ is such that $Y^{(k)}(t,\omega) = X(t,\omega)$, yields that $\tilde{X}$ is cadlag and is a version of X ($\tilde{X}_t = X_t$ P-a.e. off the union $\bigcup_{k\in N} \{\tilde{Y}_t^{(k)} \ne Y_t^{(k)}\}$).

Renaming this version X again we see, as above, that $|X_S^{T_k}| \le k\vee|X_{T_k}|$ so that X^{T_k} is of class D. It is therefore a semimartingale with a unique special decomposition

$X^{T_k} = V^{(k)}+M^{(k)}$ (with $M_0 \equiv 0$). The uniqueness of this decomposition yields that the summands $V^{(k)}$ and $V^{(k+1)}$, as well as $M^{(k)}$ and $M^{(k+1)}$, agree on $[0,T_k]$; the stationarity of $(T_k)_{k\in\mathbb{N}}$ then implies that X is a cadlag semimartingale with a unique decomposition $X = V+M$ where V is a cadlag predictable process of locally integrable variation, and M is a local martingale such that $M_0 = 0$.

Note now that since X has left limits a.e. it has them in L^0, and that every $X_{t-} \in L^1$ by Fatou's lemma; but it is not necessarily the case that $X_{t'} \to X_{t-}$ in L^1 as $t'\uparrow t$. Counterexample: let M be the local martingale of example (4) of the section on martingales and local martingales. Here M is not a martingale but for $n \in \mathbb{N}$: $M_{n+1}/\mathcal{T}_n = M_n$ (false for n+1 set as $+\infty$). Therefore M is a quasimartingale with the (QM) inequality telescoping down to $\mathbb{E}|(M_{+\infty}-M_n)/\mathcal{T}_n| = \mathbb{E}|M_n| = 1$ i.e. we can take $K = 1$. However when $n \to +\infty$ $M_n \to M_{+\infty} = 0$ while $\mathbb{E}M_n = 1 \neq 0 = \mathbb{E}M_{+\infty}$.

We say that a process X, right continuous in probability, is a *local quasimartingale* if there exist stopping times $(T_n)_{n\in\mathbb{N}}$, $T_n\uparrow\uparrow\overline{+\infty}$, such that X^{T_n} is a quasimartingale for each $n \in \mathbb{N}$. The reasoning in the previous paragraphs tells us that local quasimartingales are locally class D quasimartingales. Using the stationarity of $(T_n)_{n\in\mathbb{N}}$ and the uniqueness of the special decomposition for each X^{T_n} (with the martingale summand normalized to zero at time zero) we see that the summands are consistent in $n \in \mathbb{N}$, and so induce a unique (global) decomposition of X, the local quasimartingale, into $X = V+M$ where V is cadlag and predictable and of locally integrable variation,* and M is a local martingale with $M_0 = 0$. Local quasimartingales are also called special semimartingales.

Suppose M is a square integrable martingale. Then $(M)^2$ is a positive submartingale and hence a quasimartingale of class D. Therefore we have the unique special decomposition $(M)^2 = V+N$ where V is a cadlag predictable process of integrable variation and N is a martingale with $N_0 = 0$. Moreover it follows from the relation $\rho_{(M)^2}(]S,T[) = \mathbb{E}[(M_T)^2-(M_S)^2] \geq 0$ that V is increasing because $\mathbb{E}\int H dV = \rho_{(M)^2}(H)$ is non-negative whenever H, bounded and predictable, is. The usual notation for V is $\langle M,M\rangle$. Thus $\langle M,M\rangle$ is the unique cadlag predictable increasing process of integrable variation such that $(M)^2 - \langle M,M\rangle$ is a martingale which is zero at time zero.

More generally we can, in the same way, construct $\langle M,M\rangle$ for a locally square integrable local martingale (just insert the word 'local' at the appropriate places in the previous paragraph) to obtain the characterization: $\langle M,M\rangle$ is the unique increasing cadlag predictable process of locally

---

(*) See the remark at the end of this section.

integrable variation such that $(M)^2 - \langle M,M\rangle$ is a local martingale, zero at time zero.

Finally, given two local martingales M,N we can express the product MN as a difference of two local quasimartingales by the polarization formula :

$$MN = \frac{1}{4}[(M+N)^2 - (M-N)^2]$$

and so we can define the bilinear *oblique bracket* $\langle M,N\rangle$, when both are locally square integrable, by a similar polarization formula:

$$\langle M,N\rangle = \frac{1}{4}[\langle M+N,M+N\rangle - \langle M-N,M-N\rangle]$$

to obtain the unique cadlag predictable process of locally integrable variation such that $MN - \langle M,N\rangle$ is a local martingale, zero at time zero.

As a final remark we mention that it is not hard to show that a cadlag predictable process is locally bounded, and so is automatically locally integrable. In particular this applies to the characterization above of $\langle M,N\rangle$.

CHAPTER 2

REAL STOCHASTIC INTEGRATION

1. ORIENTATION

In this chapter we shall outline the modern theory of real stochastic integration, i.e. we shall try to give a natural meaning to $\int_{]0,+\infty]} H_s dX_s$ where X, the integrator, is a semimartingale and H a bounded (predictable) process. Note that the integration involves $]0,+\infty]$ and not $[0,+\infty]$ in compliance with our philosophy concerning time zero.

If $X = V$ is a process of finite variation and H a bounded $\mathcal{O}\otimes\mathcal{B}$ measurable process then the integration may be carried out pathwise in the sense of Stieltjes, and $J(\omega) := \int_{]0,+\infty]} H_s(\omega)dV_s(\omega)$ will be $\mathbb{P}$-measurable. If $X = M$ is a (local) martingale then in general its sample paths are of unbounded variation in any time interval (consider e.g. Brownian motion) and so any successful definition will have to be global i.e. on $\bar{\mathbb{R}}_+ \times \Omega$, yielding not a function of $\omega \in \Omega$, as J above, but a function defined up to $\mathbb{P}$-negligibility on Ω.

However, to justify the integral notation, the end product of our labour should behave as an integral. For instance it should be a map which is linear in H as well as continuous in some sense - a dominated convergence theorem would be apt. Also it would be hideous if $\int_{]0,+\infty]} 1_{]t_1,t_2]}\, dX_s$ were not equal to $X_{t_2}-X_{t_1}$.

These few natural demands in fact suffice to enable us to accomplish our goal. The guiding principle is the same as that underlying the Stieltjes theory of integration on $[0,+\infty]$. Recall that there is a one-one correspondence between cadlag functions V of finite variation normalized by $V(0) = 0$ and measures μ on $(\bar{\mathbb{R}}_+,\mathcal{B})$ such that $\mu(\{0\}) = 0$, given by $V \mapsto \mu_V$ where $\mu_V(]a,b]) \equiv \mu_V(1_{]a,b]}) := V(b)-V(a)$ and conversely $\mu \mapsto V_\mu$ where $V_\mu(x) = \mu(]0,x])$. Thus $\mu_V(]a,b]) = \int_{]0,+\infty]} 1_{]a,b]}\, dV$, in the usual notation.

In strict analogy, replacing $(\bar{\mathbb{R}}_+,\mathcal{B})$ by $(\bar{\mathbb{R}}_+\times\Omega, \text{Pre})$, deterministic intervals]a,b] by stochastic intervals]S,T], and V with a semimartingale X with $X_0=0$, we are led to seek for a construction of $\mu_X(H) = \int_{]0,+\infty]} H_s dX_s$ such that $\mu_X(]S,T]) \equiv \mu_X(1_{]S,T]}) \equiv \int_{]0,+\infty]} 1_{]S,T]} dX \equiv \int_{]S,T]} dX :=$ X_T-X_S. The analogous "inverse" map $\mu \mapsto X_{(\mu)}$ is given by

$(X_{(\mu)})_t = \mu(]0,t])$ (here $]0,t]$ denotes a stochastic interval); if $X=Y$ $\mathbb{P}$-almost everywhere (i.e. except on a $\mathbb{P}$-negligible subset of $\bar{\mathbb{R}}_+ \times \Omega$) then $\mu_X = \mu_Y$. One major difference between the two settings is that in the former, μ_V was a finite dimensional (one dimensional, actually) vector-valued measure whereas in the latter, μ_X would generally be an infinite dimensional vector-valued measure (unless $\mathcal{O}$ consists of a finite number of atoms) — $\mu_X(]S,T]) = X_T - X_S$ is a $\mathbb{P}$-measurable function and not much more. The weakest continuity assumption one would naturally seek for μ_X would be that if $(H^{(n)})_{n \in \mathbb{N}}$ were a uniformly bounded sequence of predictable processes converging pointwise to H then $\mu_X(H^{(n)})$ should converge in probability to $\mu_X(H)$. Thus we are led to defining a measure with values in the non-locally convex (!) topological vector space $L^0(\Omega,\mathcal{O},\mathbb{P})$, whose definition we now recall.

<u>$L^0(\Omega,\mathcal{O},\mathbb{P})$</u> is the space of (equivalences classes of) $\mathbb{P}$-measurable real-valued functions, endowed with the topology of convergence in probability. As such L^0 is a complete metrizable non-locally convex topological vector space (in fact the convex hull of every neighbourhood of 0, [which contains some $\mathcal{V}_{\varepsilon,\varepsilon} = \{f \in L^0 : \mathbb{P}\{|f| > \varepsilon\} < \varepsilon\}$ by definition] is generally L^0 itself if there are no atoms). Since L^0 is a metric space we can work equally well with neighbourhoods or sequences. A sequence $(f_n)_{n \in \mathbb{N}} \subset L^0$ converges to 0 in

probability iff $\forall\varepsilon > 0 \ \lim_{n\to+\infty} \mathbb{P}\{|f_n| > \varepsilon\} = 0$ iff every subsequence of $(f_n)_{n\in\mathbb{N}}$ contains a further subsequence which converges almost everywhere.

Note that $\mathcal{P}_o := \{]S,T]: S,T$ stopping times$\}$ forms a determining class i.e. μ_X on Pre, if it exists (it will), is uniquely determined by its values on $\mathcal{P}_o$ which have already been prescribed. In other words the stochastic integral (resp. the equivalent L^0-valued measure on Pre) will be independent of the method used to construct it (resp. extend it from $\mathcal{P}_o$).

We digress for a moment to discuss vector-valued measures. Let $(\Omega,\mathcal{O})$ be a measurable space and E a complete metrizable topological vector space. Denote by $\underline{B\mathcal{O}}$ the space of bounded $\mathcal{O}$-measurable real-valued functions on Ω, furnished with the sup norm topology; $\|\varphi\| := \sup_{\Omega} |\varphi|$. An E-valued measure on $(\Omega,\mathcal{O})$ is either one of the following two equivalent objects:

1) a function $\mu:\mathcal{O} \to E$ such that

(i) $A = \sum_{i=1}^{+\infty} A_n$ (disjoint), $A_n \in \mathcal{O}$, $\Rightarrow \mu(A) = \sum_{n=1}^{+\infty} \mu(A_n)$

(ii) the convex hull of $\{\mu(A):A \in \mathcal{O}\}$ is bounded,

Or 2) a (continuous) linear map $\mu:B\mathcal{O} \to E$ for which:

$(\varphi_n)_{n\in\mathbb{N}} \subset B\mathcal{O}$ such that $\varphi_n \to 0$ pointwise with $\|\varphi_n\| = \sup_{\Omega} |\varphi| \leq 1$, implies that $\mu(\varphi_n) \to 0$ in E.

We denote the collection of E-valued measures on $(\Omega,\mathcal{O})$ by Meas$(\Omega,\mathcal{O},E)$.

Remarks. (a) In condition 1)(i) the series is understood to be unconditionally convergent i.e. convergent to a fixed sum independent of the arrangement of $(A_n)_{n\in\mathbb{N}}$.

(b) Condition 1)(ii) is automatically satisfied if E is a Banach space. In this case it suffices to show that $\{\mu(A): A \in \mathcal{O}\}$ is bounded which can easily be established by way of contradiction.

(c) It is interesting to note that for L^0-valued countably additive set functions on $\mathcal{O}$, the case in which we are interested, condition 1)(ii) is always satisfied. This is a theorem of Talagrand.

(d) The equivalence between 1) and 2) follows much in the same way as for real-valued measures.

(e) Our route will be to construct the stochastic integral as an L^0-valued measure according to the second characterization.

Returning to the topic of stochastic integration, we can summarize by saying that we are seeking a (necessarily unique) $L^0(\Omega,\mathcal{O},P)$-valued measure μ_X on $(\mathfrak{R},\mathcal{O})$ where $\mathfrak{R} = \overline{\mathbb{R}}_+\times\Omega$ and $\mathcal{O}$ = Pre. This point of view seems to have originated with Pellaumail. In the next sections we will give a sketch of the construction and a converse $(\mu \mapsto X_{(\mu)})$ as well as some consequences. Briefly, we will admit a difficult decomposition theorem which reduces the work to extending $\mu_X := \mu_V+\mu_M$ where $X = V+M$ and where V is of finite variation and M is locally square integrable. Here μ_V is taken in the usual sense of Stieltjes and μ_M will be constructed locally, in a consistent manner, by means of an L^2 isometry; $\mu_M(1_{]0,t]}\ M)$ will turn out to be only a local martingale in general, even if M is a martingale. In fact if $\mu_M(1_{]0,t]}\ M)$ is a martingale for every bounded predictable process H, then the local martingale M is actually a martingale such that $E[M,M]_{+\infty}^{1/2} < +\infty$.*

We close this section with a feature of the theory of stochastic integration of unbounded predictable processes which may appear strange (even hideous), **but** only reinforces the fact that semimartingales form a minimal "stable" class. Neither the processes of finite variation nor local martingales are stable classes under stochastic integration i.e. there exist discontinuous martingales of finite variation, say M, and μ_M-integrable processes H such that $\mu_M(1_{]0,t]}\cdot H) \equiv \int_{]0,t]} HdM$ is neither of finite variation nor a local martingale but still, as always, a semimartingale. Also if V is a process of finite variation and H is μ_V-integrable then it may happen that H is nowhere Stieltjes integrable with respect to V. We will come back to this point later.

---

* See Ch. 3 for the definition of the square brackets process [M,M].

2. OUTLINE OF CONSTRUCTION

Throughout this and the next section we shall use the shorthand notation $\mathcal{R} = (\mathbb{R}_+ \times \Omega)\backslash(\{0\}\times\Omega)$ and $\mathcal{P} = \text{Pre}$.

We begin with the special case $X = V$ a cadlag process of finite variation. If H is a bounded predictable process then we define $\mu_V(H)(\omega)$ as the Stieltjes integral $\int_{]0,+\infty]} H_s(\omega)dV_s(\omega)$ and denote the process $\int_{]0,+\infty]} 1_{]0,t]}(s)H_s(\omega)dV_s(\omega) = \int_{]0,t]} H_s(\omega)dV_s(\omega)$ by $(H\cdot V)(t,\omega)$.

Next we deal with the case $X = M$, a square integrable martingale. In this case we show that μ_M extends to a continuous linear map $\mu_M : B\mathcal{P} \to L^2(\Omega,\mathcal{P},\mathbb{P})$.

Let $H = \sum_n c_n 1_{]S_n,T_n]}$ where $c_n \in B\mathcal{T}_{S_n}$ and without loss of generality, $S_0 \leq T_0 \leq S_1 \leq T_1 \leq \ldots$ Then $\mu_M(H) = \sum_n c_n(M_{T_n} - M_{S_n})$ is clearly square integrable. Since, for $S \leq T \leq S' \leq T'$:

$$\mathbb{E}\{(M_T - M_S)(M_{T'} - M_{S'})\} = \mathbb{E}\{(M_T - M_S)([M_{T'} - M_{S'}]/\mathcal{T}_T)\},$$

we can calculate $\|\mu_M(H)\|_{L^2}$ as follows:

$$\begin{aligned}\|\mu_M(\sum_n c_n 1_{]S_n,T_n]})\|^2_{L^2} &= \mathbb{E}\sum_n c_n^2(M_{T_n} - M_{S_n})^2 \\ &= \mathbb{E}\sum_n c_n^2([M^2_{T_n} - 2M_{T_n}M_{S_n} + M^2_{S_n}]/\mathcal{T}_{S_n}) \\ &= \mathbb{E}\sum_n c_n^2(M^2_{T_n} - M^2_{S_n}) \\ &= \mathbb{E}\sum_n c_n^2(\langle M,M\rangle_{T_n} - \langle M,M\rangle_{S_n})\end{aligned}$$

$$= \mathbb{E}\mu_{<M,M>}(H^2) \text{ or } \mathbb{E}\int_{]0,+\infty]} H_s^2 d<M,M>_s .$$

Thus we can extend μ_M as an isometry from $L^2(\Omega,\mathcal{P}, d\mathbb{P}(\omega)d<M,M>_s(\omega))$ into $L^2(\Omega,\mathcal{O},\mathbb{P})$. Now $B\mathcal{P} \hookrightarrow L^2(\Omega,\mathcal{P}, d\mathbb{P}(\omega)d<M,M>_s(\omega))$; and $H_{(n)} \to 0$ pointwise and boundedly implies that $\mu_M(H_{(n)}) \to 0$ in $L^2(\Omega,\mathcal{O},\mathbb{P})$ and hence in $L^0(\Omega,\mathcal{O},P)$. Therefore this extension restricted to $B\mathcal{P}$ is the one we were seeking. We denote a cadlag version of the martingale $\mu_M(1_{]0,t]}H) \equiv \int_{]0,t]} H_s dM_s$ by $(H.M)_t$.

For $X = V+M$ where V is of finite variation and M a square integrable martingale we define $\mu_X = \mu_V+\mu_M$ and $H\cdot X = H\cdot V+H\cdot M$. That these definitions are independent of the decomposition used can easily be checked for $H \in \mathcal{P}_o$ first, from which it follows in general.

We now list some important properties of the stochastic integral $H\cdot X$ when $X = V+M$ is of the preceding form, and where N (appearing below) is a square integrable martingale:

1) $H\cdot X$ is a semimartingale; $H\cdot V$ is predictable and of integrable variation, and $H\cdot M$ is a square integrable martingale.

2) $H\cdot(K\cdot X) = (HK)\cdot X$

3) $<H\cdot M, K\cdot N> = (HK)\cdot<M,N>$

4) $(H\cdot X)^T = H\cdot X^T = (H1_{]0,T]})\cdot X$

5) $<M,N>^T = <M^T,N> = <M,N^T> = <M^T,N^T>$ (these relations may not appear at first sight to involve stochastic integra-

tion, but they are consequences of the previous properties).

6) $\Delta(H\cdot X) = H(\Delta X)$ $(\Delta X_t := X_t - X_{t-}$, etc.) $\mathbb{P}$-a.e. (i.e. off a $\mathbb{P}$-negligible subset of $\bar{\mathbb{R}}_+\times\Omega$).

The extension of the stochastic integral from the special case of a square integrable martingale to that of a local martingale rests on a hard theorem which we merely state.

Theorem. A local martingale M can be expressed as a sum $M = M_{(1)}+M_{(2)}$ with $M_{(1)}$ a local martingale of locally integrable variation and $M_{(2)}$ a local martingale which is locally square integrable.

With the aid of this theorem we can define H·M locally and consistently as follows. Let $(T_n)_{n\in\mathbb{N}}$ be a localizing sequence of stopping times for the decomposition $M = M_{(1)}+M_{(2)}$ as in the theorem. Then define $(H\cdot M)^{T_n} := (H\cdot M_{(1)})^{T_n} + (H\cdot M_{(2)})^{T_n} = H\cdot M_{(1)}^{T_n} + H\cdot M_{(2)}^{T_n}$, for H a bounded predictable process. That this definition is independent of the decomposition used can be seen by looking at $H \in \mathcal{P}_o$ firstly; in particular $(1_{]S,T]}\cdot M)^{T_n} = M^{T_n\wedge T} - M^{T_n\wedge S}$. It is also easy to check that $(H\cdot M)^{T_n} = (H\cdot M)^{T_{n+1}}$ on $]0,T_n]$, so by the stationarity of $(T_n)_{n\in\mathbb{N}}$ we have a well defined process H·M which is in fact a semimartingale.

The extension to the measure μ_M is now evident $-\mu_M(H) = (H\cdot M)_{+\infty}$. For the general case of a semimartingale X, we set $\mu_X = \mu_V + \mu_M$.

We mention one property contrasting the behaviour of the jumps of a general semimartingale X with that of a process of finite variation, which is a consequence of the theorem stated above. For a process V of finite variation, $\sum_s |\Delta V_s| < +\infty$. For a square integrable martingale M, $\sum_s (\Delta M_s)^2 < +\infty$ a.e. . Indeed, for any subdivision $t_0 = 0 < t_1 < \ldots < t_n = +\infty$ of $\bar{\mathbb{R}}_+$: $\mathbb{E} \sum_{i=0}^{n-1} |M_{t_i+1} - M_{t_i}|^2 = \mathbb{E} \sum_{i=0}^{n-1} (\langle M,M\rangle_{t_{i+1}} - \langle M,M\rangle_{t_i}) = \mathbb{E}(\langle M,M\rangle_{+\infty} - M_0^2)$. By a limiting process $\sum_s |\Delta M_s|^2 \leq \liminf_{n\to+\infty} \sum_{i=0}^{n-1} |M_{t_{i+1}^n} - M_{t_i^n}|^2$, where $(t_i^n)_{i=0}^n$ is a sequence of subdivisions of $\bar{\mathbb{R}}_+$ such that $\lim_{n\to+\infty} \max_{0\leq i\leq n-2} (t_{i+1}^n - t_i^n) = 0$ and $\lim_{n\to+\infty} t_{n-1}^n = +\infty$. By Fatou's lemma $\mathbb{E} \sum_s |\Delta M_s|^2 \leq \mathbb{E}\langle M,M\rangle_{+\infty} < +\infty$; therefore $\sum_s (\Delta M_s)^2 < +\infty$ $\mathbb{P}$-a.e. Thus by the decomposition theorem stated above and a, by now, familiar "localizing and stationarity" argument we conclude that $\sum_s (\Delta X_s)^2 < +\infty$ $\mathbb{P}$-a.e.

We summarize the work of this section in the form of a theorem.

<u>Fundamental Theorem</u>. A semimartingale X, with $X_0 = 0$, determines (i.e. the equivalence class of semimartingales

which coincide with X off some $\mathbb{P}$-negligible subset of $]0,+\infty]\times\Omega$ does) a unique $L^0(\Omega,\mathcal{O},\mathbb{P})$-valued measure μ_X on $]0,+\infty]\times\Omega$, equipped with the predictable σ-algebra, such that for S,T stopping times with $S \leq T$: $\mu_X(]S,T]) = X_T - X_S$. For H a bounded predictable function on $]0,+\infty]\times\Omega$, $\mu_X(H)$ is also written $\int_{]0,+\infty]} H_s dX_s$; $\int_{]0,+\infty]} H_s 1_{]0,t]}(s) dX_s$ is also written $\int_{]0,t]} H_s dX_s$ or $(H\cdot X)_t$. It is a semimartingale and called the stochastic integral of H with respect to X. □

We extend the definition of stochastic integration to a semimartingale X for which X_0 is not necessarily 0 by setting $\mu_X := \mu_{X-X_0}$; we will write $\mu_X(H) \equiv \int_{]0,+\infty]} H_s dX_s$ though. As such μ_X can be trivially extended to $[0,+\infty]\times\Omega$ by declaring $\{0\}\times\Omega$ to be μ_X-negligible.

We close this section with two examples concerning μ_X (or dX) - integrability in the case where X is a process of finite variation. That is, for a general semimartingale X we have constructed the measure μ_X on Pre. One can then speak of integration of unbounded predictable processes with respect to μ_X (for more details see the section on integrability). In the case where X is of finite variation, the integration, which is à la Stieltjes for bounded predictable integrands, can be performed for merely $\mathcal{O}\otimes\mathcal{B}$ measurable integrands. Calling this latter measure (on $\mathcal{O}\otimes\mathcal{B}$) $\tilde{\mu}_X$, μ_X and $\tilde{\mu}_X$ are radically different in at least one respect which we shall describe presently.

Integrabilility with respect to $\tilde{\mu}_X$ is stronger than integrability with respect to μ_X. This was alluded to, in the orientation section. For instance, let $(J_n)_{n\in\mathbb{N}}$ be an i.i.d. sequence with $\mathbb{P}\{J_1=1\} = \frac{1}{2} = \mathbb{P}\{J_1=-1\}$ and $(a_n)_{n\in\mathbb{N}}$ a positive sequence with $\sum_n a_n^2 < +\infty$ and $\sum_n a_n = +\infty$. Define $X_t = \sum_{n\leq t} a_n^2 J_n$ and $H_t = 1/a_n$ on $]n-1,n]$. Then $\mu_X(H) = \sum_n a_n J_n < +\infty$ a.e. but $\sum_n \frac{1}{a_n} a_n^2 |J_n| = +\infty$ so that H is not Stieltjes $\tilde{\mu}_X$-integrable.

Considering $\tilde{\mu}_X$ as an extension of μ_X from Pre to $\mathcal{O}\otimes\mathcal{B}$, their Lebesgue extensions $\hat{\tilde{\mu}}_X$ and $\hat{\mu}_X$ to the completions of these σ-algebras are related: $\hat{\mu}_X$ is larger than $\hat{\tilde{\mu}}_X$. This phenomenon is of a general nature which we can illustrate in a simpler setting. Take $\Omega = [0,1]$ and $\mathcal{A} = \{\phi,\Omega\} \subset \mathcal{B}$ the Borel σ-algebra of $[0,1]$. Then a Lebesgue integrable $\hat{\mathcal{A}} = \mathcal{A}$ measurable function is constant while the $\hat{\mathcal{B}}$ (Lebesgue measurable) ones are evidently not necessarily so. On the other hand, if μ is a Radon measure on Ω with $\mu(\Omega) = 0$ then the Lebesgue extension $\hat{\mu}$ on $\hat{\mathcal{A}} = 2^{\Omega}$ is identically zero so that all functions are integrable - even non-$\hat{\mathcal{B}}$ measurable ones. Moreover, in this case, even when both integrals (with respect to $\hat{\mathcal{A}}$ and $\hat{\mathcal{B}}$) are defined, they need not coincide. Thus in general the completions of a measure μ, with respect to $\mathcal{A} \subset \mathcal{B}$, are incomparable.

3. INVERSE PROBLEM; CONSEQUENCES

In this section we outline the solution of the inverse problem of stochastic integration, due to Dellacherie, which is that of associating with certain $L^0(\Omega,\mathcal{O},\mathbb{P})$-valued measures μ, a semimartingale $X_{(\mu)}$ such that $\mu \mapsto X_{(\mu)}$ is inverse to $X \mapsto \mu_X$ as constructed in the previous section. Before delving into the solution of this difficult problem, it is necessary that we describe two properties which μ should enjoy.

An $L^0(\Omega,\mathcal{O},\mathbb{P})$-valued measure μ is said to be *adapted in time* if whenever $H \in B\mathcal{O}$ is supported in $]0,t]\times\Omega$ then $\mu(H) \in \mathcal{T}_t$. An $L^0(\Omega,\mathcal{O},\mathbb{P})$-valued measure is said to be *localizable* if whenever $H \in B\mathcal{O}$ is supported in $\bar{\mathbb{R}}_+\times\Omega_0$, with $\Omega_0 \subset \Omega$ i.e. $H = 0$ outside $\bar{\mathbb{R}}_+\times\Omega_0$, then $\mu(H)$ is supported in Ω_0 (note that $\bar{\mathbb{R}}_+\times\Omega_0$ is not predictable). The significance of this property is that if $H_{(1)} = H_{(2)}$ on $\bar{\mathbb{R}}_+\times\Omega_0$, $\Omega_0 \subset \Omega$, then $\mu(H_{(1)}) = \mu(H_{(2)})$ on Ω_0. Both of these properties are enjoyed by the class of semimartingale measures μ_X, the latter being a simple case of theorem (4) in the section on Theorems of Equivalence. Conversely, we have the following theorem due to Dellacherie.

<u>Theorem.</u> To every $L^0(\Omega,\mathcal{O},\mathbb{P})$-valued measure μ on $(\bar{\mathbb{R}}_+\times\Omega\setminus\{0\}\times\Omega,\ \mathrm{Pre})$ which is adapted in time and localizable there corresponds a unique (up to $\mathbb{P}$-negligibility) semimartingale X, such that $X_0=0$, and $\mu_X=\mu$.

<u>Sketch of proof</u>. Considering $B\mathcal{O}$ now with the sup norm topology, it is a commutative C*-algebra and hence isomorphic to $C(K)$ for some compact topological space K by a theorem of Gelfand. Since μ remains continuous when considered as a linear map of $C(K) \cong B\mathcal{O}$ (the Banach space) into $L^0(\Omega,\mathcal{O},\mathbb{P})$ we can use the following factorization which follows from the work of B. Maurey:

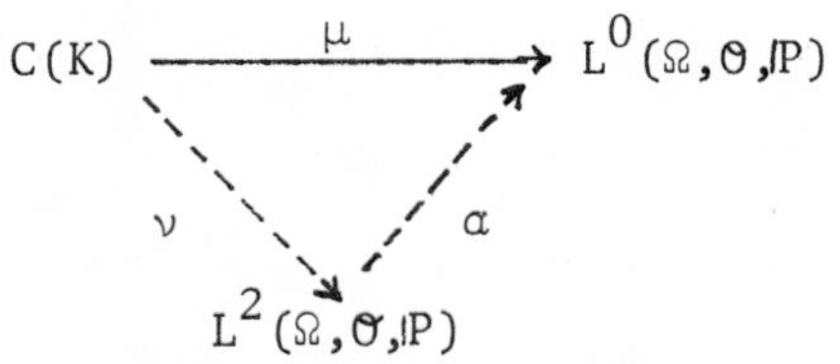

where $\alpha:\Omega \to \mathbb{R}$ is measurable and acts as a multiplication operator: $\mu = \alpha\nu$. (Such a factorization was obtained by Grothendieck with L^0 replaced by L^1.)

Define a probability $\mathbb{Q}$ on $(\Omega,\mathcal{O})$ by $\mathbb{Q} = \dfrac{c}{1+\alpha^2}\mathbb{P}$, where $c^{-1} = \mathbb{E}^{\mathbb{P}}[(1+\alpha^2)^{-1}]$ is a normalizing constant, and consider μ as a map into $L^0(\Omega,\mathcal{O},\mathbb{Q})$. For $\varphi \in B\mathcal{O}$:

$$[\mathbb{E}^{\mathbb{Q}}|\mu(\varphi)|]^2 \le \mathbb{E}^{\mathbb{Q}}[\mu(\varphi)]^2 = \mathbb{E}^{\mathbb{P}}[c(1+\alpha^2)^{-1}\cdot\alpha^2|\nu(\varphi)|^2]$$

$$\le c\|\nu\|^2\cdot\|\varphi\|^2$$

i.e. the image under $\mu:B\mathcal{O} \to L^0(\Omega,\mathcal{O},\mathbb{Q})$ of a bounded set is a bounded subset of $L^1(\Omega,\mathcal{O},\mathbb{Q})$.

The relation between μ and X is evident - $X_t=\mu(]0,t]\times\Omega)$, which is adapted since μ is so, by hypothesis. Also, since μ

is localizable we have more generally that $\mu(H1_{]s,t]}) = H(X_t - X_s)$ for $H \in B\mathcal{T}_s$. It suffices to check this for $H = 1_A$, $A \in \mathcal{T}_s$:

$$1_A(X_t - X_s) = 1_A\mu(]s,t]\times\Omega) = 1_A\mu(]s,t]\times A) + 1_A\mu(]s,t]\times A^c)$$
$$= \mu(]s,t]\times A), \text{ since } \mu \text{ is localizable.}$$

By the Girsanov property, X being a $\mathbb{P}$-semimartingale will follow from X being a $\mathbb{Q}$-quasimartingale, which we now show. Let $\pi = \{t_i\}$ be a partition of $\bar{\mathbb{R}}_+$; then

$$\mathbb{E}^{\mathbb{Q}}\sum_i |(X_{t_{i+1}} - X_{t_i})/\mathcal{T}_i| = \mathbb{E}^{\mathbb{Q}}\sum_i [(X_{t_{i+1}} - X_{t_i})/\mathcal{T}_i]\cdot\mathrm{sgn}[(X_{t_{i+1}} - X_{t_i})/\mathcal{T}_i]$$
$$= \mathbb{E}^{\mathbb{Q}}\sum_i (X_{t_{i+1}} - X_{t_i})\,\mathrm{sgn}[(X_{t_{i+1}} - X_{t_i})/\mathcal{T}_i]$$

(condition $/\mathcal{T}_i$ the line above to obtain the first line)

$$= \mathbb{E}^{\mathbb{Q}}\mu(\sum_i \mathrm{sgn}[(X_{t_{i+1}} - X_{t_i})/\mathcal{T}_i]1_{]t_i,t_{i+1}]})$$
$$\equiv \mathbb{E}^{\mathbb{Q}}\mu(H_\pi) \le c^{\frac{1}{2}}\|\nu\|\|H_\pi\| \le c^{\frac{1}{2}}\|\nu\|.$$

Since $\mathbb{P}(|X_s - X_t| \ge \varepsilon) = \mathbb{P}(|\mu(]s,t])| \ge \varepsilon) \to 0$, as $t \to s$, because μ is an L^0-valued measure, X is right continuous in probability with respect to $\mathbb{P}$ and hence $\mathbb{Q}$. Thus X is a $\mathbb{Q}$-quasimartingale, and so has a cadlag version. We have already seen that μ_X and μ agree on a generating set for BPre. □

We mention three rather immediate consequences of this correspondance theorem which would be hard to obtain without it. The completeness assumption on the σ-algebras $(\mathcal{T}_t)_{t\in\bar{\mathbb{R}}_+}$ will be dropped for this discussion.

Firstly if $\mathcal{S} \subset \mathcal{T}$ is a smaller filtration then an $\mathcal{S}$-adapted process X which is a $\mathcal{T}$-semimartingale is also an $\mathcal{S}$-semimartingale. To see this, just restrict μ_X to $\mathcal{S}$ (adaptation comes into play here) thereby obtaining an $\mathcal{S}$-semimartingale Y such that $Y_t = \mu_X(]0,t]\times\Omega) = X_t$.

Secondly, if X is a $\mathbb{P}$-semimartingale and $\mathbb{Q} << \mathbb{P}$ then X is also a $\mathbb{Q}$-semimartingale. Indeed, the identity map id: $L^0(\Omega,\mathcal{O},\mathbb{P}) \hookrightarrow L^0(\Omega,\mathcal{O},\mathbb{Q})$ is continuous so we may consider μ_X as an $L^0(\Omega,\mathcal{O},\mathbb{Q})$-valued measure. From it we obtain a $\mathbb{Q}$-semimartingale which is evidently equal to X.

Thirdly, if X is simultaneously a $\mathbb{P}$ and $\mathbb{Q}$-semimartingale then it is also a $\frac{\mathbb{P}+\mathbb{Q}}{2}$-semimartingale. To see this, define $\tilde{\mu}: B\mathcal{O} \to \mathcal{L}^0(\Omega,\mathcal{O},\frac{\mathbb{P}+\mathbb{Q}}{2})$ ($\mathcal{L}^0$ denotes L^0 prior to taking equivalence classes; $\pi: \mathcal{L}^0 \to L^0$ will denote the quotient map) on simple functions $H = \sum_i H_i 1_{]s_i,t_i]}$, with $H_i \in \mathcal{T}_{s_i}$ by $\tilde{\mu}(H) = \sum_i H_i(X_{t_i} - X_{s_i})$. If $(H^{(n)})_{n\in\mathbb{N}}$ is a Cauchy sequence in $B\mathcal{O}$ then we know that $(\tilde{\mu}(H^{(n)})_{n\in\mathbb{N}}$ is Cauchy in both $\mathcal{L}^0(\Omega,\mathcal{O},\mathbb{P})$ and $\mathcal{L}^0(\Omega,\mathcal{O},\mathbb{Q})$, and hence also in $\mathcal{L}^0(\Omega,\mathcal{O},\frac{\mathbb{P}+\mathbb{Q}}{2})$. Thus $\tilde{\mu}$ extends to a continuous linear map: $\tilde{\mu}: B\mathcal{O} \to \mathcal{L}^0(\Omega,\mathcal{O},\frac{\mathbb{P}+\mathbb{Q}}{2})$, and the measure $\tilde{\mu} := \pi\circ\tilde{\mu}: B\mathcal{O} \to L^0(\Omega,\mathcal{O},\frac{\mathbb{P}+\mathbb{Q}}{2})$ corresponds to a $\frac{\mathbb{P}+\mathbb{Q}}{2}$-semimartingale which is equal, up to negligibility ($\mathbb{P}$ or $\mathbb{Q}$), to X. This result implies that there always exists a common version of a stochastic integral with respect to X which coincides with those constructed with respect to any two probability measures.

4. THE OPTIONAL INTEGRAL

In this section we show how stochastic integration may be extended to include optional integrands. Let X be a real valued continuous semimartingale and $H \in \mathrm{Opt}$ real valued.

We say that a subset $A \subset \bar{\mathbb{R}}_+ \times \Omega$ has *denumerable sections* if almost every $A(\omega)$ is a denumerable subset of $\bar{\mathbb{R}}_+$.

We begin with the observation that given $H \in \mathrm{Opt}$ we can find an $H' \in \mathrm{Pre}$ differing from H only on a set having denumerable sections; if $H \in \mathrm{BOpt}$ we can take $H' \in \mathrm{BPre}$. For instance if $H = 1_{|S,T|}$, $|S,T|$ denoting an arbitrary stochastic interval, then we can take $H' = 1_{]S,T]}$. Also if H is cadlag, we can take $H' = H_-$. More generally, if $H \in \mathrm{Opt}$, $(H_{(n)})_{n \in \mathbb{N}}$ are optional with $H_{(n)} \to H$ pointwise as $n \to +\infty$, and $H'_{(n)}$ is any predictable process differing from $H_{(n)}$ only on a set having denumerable sections, then we can take H' to be $\lim_{n \to +\infty} H'_{(n)}$ on the predictable set where the limit exists and zero on the complement. If H is bounded then we can truncate H' by the bounds of H. Our claim then follows from the functional form of the Monotone Class theorem. We denote the class of all such H' by H^{Pre}, with the understanding that elements of the latter are bounded if H is bounded, and moreover have the same bounds.

If $H \in \mathrm{BOpt}$ and $H', H'' \in H^{\mathrm{Pre}}$ then H'' differs from H' only on a predictable set having denumerable sections. Such a set is contained in a countable union of graphs of predictable stopping times $(T_n)_{n\in\mathbb{N}}$; this fact can be derived as a corollary to Dellacherie's predictable section theorem. If T denotes one of these stopping times with $T_n' \uparrow T$ on $\{T > 0\}$ then

$$\mu_X([T]) = \lim_{n\to+\infty} \mu_X(]T_n',T]) + \mu_X(\{0\}\times\{T=0\})$$

$$= \lim_{n\to+\infty} (X_T - X_{T_n'}) + 0$$

$$= \begin{cases} X_T - X_{T-}, & \text{on } \{T>0\} \\ X_0 - X_0, & \text{on } \{T=0\}, \end{cases}$$

so $\mu_X([T])=0$ since X is continuous. Thus we can unambiguously define $H\cdot X$ for $H \in BOpt$ and X a continuous semimartingale by $H'\cdot X$ for any $H' \in H^{Pre}$: for $H'' \in H^{Pre}$, $(H'-H'')\cdot X = (H'-H'')\cdot(\sum_n [1_{\{H'\neq H''\}}\cdot(1_{[T_n]}\cdot X)]$, and $(1_{[T_n]}\cdot X)_t = \mu_{X^t}([T_n]) = 0$ (that $1_{[T_n]}\cdot X = 0$, can also be derived as above with X_T replaced by X^T, etc.).

Denoting $(H\cdot X)_{+\infty}$ (H and X as above) by $\mathring{\mu}_X(H)$ we can show that $\mathring{\mu}_X$ is on $L^0(\Omega,\mathcal{O},\mathbb{P})$-valued measure on $(\bar{\mathbb{R}}_+\times\Omega, Opt)$. Indeed if $(H_{(n)})_{n\in\mathbb{N}} \subset BOpt$ with $H_{(n)} \to 0$ as $n \to +\infty$ pointwise with $|H_{(n)}| \leq 1$ for all $n \in \mathbb{N}$ then choosing $H'_{(n)} \in H^{Pre}_{(n)}$ we have that $H'_{(n)} \to 0$ except possibly on a predictable set having denumerable sections i.e. a set of μ_X-measure zero. Therefore $\mathring{\mu}_X(H_{(n)}) = \mu_X(H'_{(n)}) \to 0$ as $n \to +\infty$.

Note that $\mathring{\mu}_X(|S,T|) = X_T - X_S$, for any stochastic interval $|S,T|$, $\mu_X(H) = \mu_X(H_-)$ if H is cadlag, and that for any stopping time T, $\mathring{\mu}_X([T]) = 0$ since $0 \in 1^{Pre}_{[T]}$. Since not every graph [T] is μ_X-measurable we see that $\mathring{\mu}_X$ is not comparable with the Lebesgue extension of μ_X.

It is easy to see that $\mathring{\mu}_X$ is both adapted and localizable. One may ask whether or not all $L^0(\Omega,\mathcal{O},\mathbb{P})$-valued adapted, localizable measures on $(\bar{\mathbb{R}}_+\times\Omega,\mathrm{Opt})$, which do not charge the graphs of stopping times, arise from a continuous semimartingale X as $\mathring{\mu}_X$. The answer is negative, being provided by the following simple counterexample. Let T be a totally inaccessible stopping time and $X = 1_{[T,+\infty]}$ (which is discontinuous), and define $\mu(H) = \mu_X(H')$ for any $H' \in H^{Pre}$, $H \in \mathrm{BOpt}$. In this instance μ is well defined because if $H'' \in H^{Pre}$ is another candidate then $H''-H'$ is zero except possibly on a predictable set, which cannot intersect [T]. Thus $\mu_X(H''-H')=0$. However $\mathring{\mu}$ is adapted, localizable and charges no graph of any stopping time S since $0 \in 1^{Pre}_{[S]}$.

In order to obtain a theorem of correspondence we must at present hypothesize in addition that the measure restricted to Pre arises from a continuous semimartingale. More precisely we have the following theorem.

Theorem. Let $\mu:\mathrm{BOpt} \to L^0(\Omega,\mathcal{O},\mathbb{P})$ be a measure not charging the graphs of stopping times, whose restriction to BPre coincides with a μ_X where X is a continuous semimartingale with $X_0=0$. Then there exists a unique continuous semimartingale zero at time 0, namely X, such that $\mu=\mathring{\mu}_X$.

One may well wonder why the theory of stochastic integration could not be carried out on Opt in a manner analogous to that for Pre, i.e., defining, for X a semimartingale, an L^0-valued set function μ_X by $\mu_X([S,T[) = X_{T\pm}-X_{S\pm}$ with any uniform choice of signs. Such a prescription simply does not extend to a measure on BOpt. For example consider the cadlag extension of the discrete time martingale $X_N = \sum_{n\leq N} a_n J_n$ where $(J_n)_{n\in\mathbb{N}}$ is an i.i.d. sequence with $\mathbb{P}(J_n=-1)=\mathbb{P}(J_n=1)=1/2$ and $(a_n)_{n\in\mathbb{N}}$ is a positive sequence such that $\sum_n a_n^2 < +\infty$ but $\sum_n a_n = +\infty$. Then any reasonable definition should yield for $H_n=J_n$: $\mu_X(H1_{[0,N]}) = \sum_{n\leq N} a_n$ which diverges as $N \to +\infty$, even though $H1_{[0,N]}$ is uniformly bounded in N, so that $\mu_X(H)$ would also not be defined. Notice that in this "example" X is discontinuous, and H is not predictable since $H_n \notin \mathcal{T}_{n-1}$.

CHAPTER 3

SEMIMARTINGALE TOPOLOGIES: SQUARE BRACKETS

(We adhere to the shorthand $\mathcal{R} = \overline{\mathbb{R}}_+\times\Omega$, $\mathcal{O}$ = Pre, $E = L^0(\Omega,\mathcal{O},\mathbb{P})$ in this chapter.)

Denote the class of square integrable martingales by $\mathcal{M}L^2$. Under the topology induced by the norm $\|M\|_2 := \|M_{+\infty}\|_{L^2}$, $\mathcal{M}L^2$ becomes a Hilbert space with inner product $\mathbb{E}(M_{+\infty}N_{+\infty})$, which is the same as $\mathbb{E}\langle M,N\rangle_{+\infty}$. It follows easily from Doob's inequality - $\|\sup_t|M_t|\|_{L^2} \leq 2\|M_{+\infty}\|_{L^2}$ - that the subspace $\mathcal{M}^cL^2$ consisting of continuous square integrable martingales which are zero at time t=0, is closed and it is evidently stable for stopping times. The orthogonal complement of $\mathcal{M}^cL^2$ is usually called the class of *purely discontinuous* martingales, which is also stable for stopping times since for $M \in (\mathcal{M}^cL^2)^\perp$, $N \in \mathcal{M}^cL^2$, and T a stopping time, $N^T \in \mathcal{M}^cL^2$ and $\mathbb{E}(M^T_{+\infty}N_{+\infty}) = \mathbb{E}\langle M^T,N\rangle_{+\infty} = \mathbb{E}\langle M,M^T\rangle_{+\infty} = 0$. The terminology "purely discontinuous" is unfortunate as such a martingale can have substantial intervals of continuity. Examples are provided by the following theorem which we admit without proof.

Theorem. A square integrable martingale of finite variation is purely discontinuous, and so identically zero if also continuous and zero at time 0.

Thus a discrete time martingale embedded into continuous time is purely discontinuous. So also is $N_t^T - T\wedge t$ where N is a Poisson process with parameter 1 and T is the first jump time (which happens to be totally inaccessible with respect to the minimal filtration).

Now for the decomposition of a semimartingale $X=V+M$ where V is of finite variation and M a locally square integrable local martingale (see p.55), with localizing sequence $(T_n)_{n\in\mathbb{N}}$, we can further decompose M^{T_n} as the sum of its continuous and purely discontinuous parts $M^{T_n}_{(c)}$ and $M^{T_n}_{(d)}$. Since

$$[M^{T_{n+1}}_{(c)\text{ or }(d)}]^{T_n} = [(M^{T_{n+1}})^{T_n}]_{(c)\text{ or }(d)} = M^{T_n}_{(c)\text{ or }(d)}$$

we have the consistency: $M^{T_{n+1}}_{(c)\text{ or }(d)} = M^{T_n}_{(c)\text{ or }(d)}$ on $[0,T_n]$. Thus a well defined decomposition $M = M^{(d)}+M^{(c)}$ arises where $M^{(c)}$ and $M^{(d)}$ are locally square integrable local martingales, $M^{(c)}$ being continuous and $M^{(d)}$ being (locally) purely discontinuous. Define $\tilde{X} = V+M^{(d)}$ and $X^{(c)} = M^{(c)}$. Then the decomposition $X = \tilde{X}+X^{(c)}$ is unique, where $X^{(c)}$ is a continuous locally square integrable local martingale with

$X_0^{(c)} = 0$, and $\tilde{X}$ is the sum of a process of finite variation, and a locally square integrable local martingale which is (locally) purely discontinuous. Indeed this follows easily from the theorem stated in this section. We refer to $\tilde{X}$ as the *characteristic* component of X.

The *square brackets* (or mutual quadratic variation) process associated with two semimartingales X and Y is a finite variation process defined through the decomposition above by

$$[X,Y] := X_0 Y_0 + \sum_{0<s\leq \cdot} \Delta X_s \Delta Y_s + \langle X^{(c)}, Y^{(c)} \rangle .$$

It can be shown that $[X,Y]_t = X_0 Y_0 + \lim \sum_{n=0}^{N-1} (X_{t_{n+1}\wedge t} - X_{t_n \wedge t}) \cdot (Y_{t_{n+1}\wedge t} - Y_{t_n\wedge t})$ where each $\{t_n\}_{n=0}^{N}$ is a partition of $\overline{\mathbb{R}}_+$, with $t_0 = 0$ and $t_N = +\infty$, and the limit is taken in probability as $\max_{1\leq n\leq N-1} (t_n - t_{n-1})$ tends to 0 and $t_{N-1} \to +\infty$ as $N \to +\infty$.

We now turn our attention to topologies for general semimartingales. Denoting by $\mathcal{SM}_0$ (resp. $\mathcal{SM}_0^c$) the class of semimartingales (resp. continuous semimartingales) which vanish at time 0, we have seen that $\mathcal{SM}_0$ is in one-one correspondence with a subset of Meas$(\Omega,\mathfrak{O},\mathbb{E})$; namely the adapted and localizable ones. Considering $B\mathfrak{O}$ with the Banach sup norm topology, we can further embed Meas$(\Omega,\mathfrak{O},\mathbb{E})$ into $\mathcal{L}(B\mathfrak{O},\mathbb{E})$, the complete metrizable space of continuous linear maps of $B\mathfrak{O}$ into $\mathbb{E}$ when endowed with the topology of uniform convergence on bounded sets. Thus we can induce a topology on $\mathcal{SM}_0$ through the inclusions: $\mathcal{SM}_0 \subset \mathrm{Meas}(\Omega,\mathcal{O},E) \subset \mathcal{L}(B\mathcal{O},E)$. It turns out that $\mathcal{SM}_0$ is a closed subset in this topology so that it also is a complete metrizable topological vector space. A neighbourhood of 0 in $\mathcal{SM}_0$ contains a set of the form

$$\mathcal{V}_{\varepsilon,\delta} = \{X \in \mathcal{SM}_0 : \forall\varphi \in B\mathcal{O} \text{ with } \|\varphi\|_\infty \leq 1,\ \mathbb{P}\{|\mu_X(\varphi)| > \delta\} \leq \varepsilon\}\ .$$

For X, a semimartingale not necessarily zero at time 0, we write $X = X_0 + X_{(0)}$ with $X_{(0)} \in \mathcal{SM}_0$ i.e. we decompose $\mathcal{SM}$, the class of semimartingales, ($\mathcal{SM}^c$ denotes the continuous ones) into a topological direct sum $\mathcal{SM} = \mathcal{T}_0 \oplus \mathcal{SM}_0$, where $\mathcal{T}_0$ carries the topology of convergence in probability (we have used the shorthand $\mathcal{T}_0$ to represent $L^0(\Omega,\mathcal{T}_0,\mathbb{P})$).

The set $\mathcal{SM}$ is also contained in the class of cadlag processes which we denote by Cadlag. We endow Cadlag with the following complete metrizable topology: $X^{(n)} \to 0$ in Cadlag if $X^{(n)*} := \sup_t |X_t^{(n)}| \to 0$ in probability. Equivalently $X^{(n)} \to X$ in Cadlag if each subsequence of $(X^{(n)})_{n\in\mathbb{N}}$ contains a further subsequence converging to X almost surely, uniformly in $t \in \overline{\mathbb{R}}_+$. However the topology $\mathcal{SM}$ carries is stronger than the restriction of the Cadlag topology. For if $(X^{(n)})_{n\in\mathbb{N}} \subset \mathcal{SM}_0$ and $X^{(n)} \to 0$ in $\mathcal{SM}_0$ then defining, for $\varepsilon > 0$, $T_n = \inf\{t : |X_t^{(n)}| \geq \varepsilon\}$, allows us to estimate:

$$\mathbb{P}\{X^{(n)*} > \varepsilon\} \leq \mathbb{P}\{|X_{T_n}^{(n)}| \geq \varepsilon\} = \mathbb{P}\{|\mu_{X^{(n)}}(]0,T_n])| \geq \varepsilon\}\ .$$

The latter quantity tends to zero as $n \to +\infty$ since $(1_{]0,T_n]})_{n\in\mathbb{N}}$ is uniformly bounded in $B\mathcal{O}$. A consequence of the continuous inclusion $\mathcal{SM} \hookrightarrow$Cadlag is that $X^{(n)} \to 0$ in $\mathcal{SM}$ implies that $\varphi\cdot X^{(n)} \to 0$ in Cadlag for each $\varphi \in B\mathcal{O}$ uniformly so for $\|\varphi\| \le 1$. Indeed, $\varphi\cdot X^{(n)} \to 0$ in $\mathcal{SM}_0$ since for $\psi \in B\mathcal{O}$: $\mu_{\varphi\cdot X^{(n)}}(\psi) = \mu_{X^{(n)}}(\varphi\psi)$ (*).

Although the topology of $\mathcal{SM}$ is stronger than that of Cadlag there is a simple instance in which they coincide. Since we will need this result in the sequel we prove it as a lemma.

<u>Lemma</u>. If $(Y^{(n)})_{n\in N} \subset \mathcal{SM}_0$ is such that each $Y^{(n)}$ vanishes off $\overline{\mathbb{R}}_+\times\Omega_n$, where $\mathbb{P}(\Omega_n) \to 0$ as $n \to +\infty$, then $Y^{(n)} \to 0$ in $\mathcal{SM}_0$ as $n \to +\infty$.

<u>Proof</u>. We must show that $Z^{(n)} := \mu_{Y^{(n)}}(\varphi) \to 0$ in $L^0(\Omega,\mathcal{O},\mathbb{P})$ as $n \to +\infty$, uniformly in $\varphi \in B\mathcal{O}$ with $\|\varphi\| \le 1$. It is not hard to show that $Z^{(n)}$ vanishes off Ω_n (this is clear for φ of the form $1_{]S,T]}$, where S,T are stopping times with $S \le T$; a standard monotone class argument leads one from the case of linear combinations of these to the general case. A generalization of this property will be given in the section on theorems of equivalence.). Therefore, given $\varepsilon > 0$

$\mathbb{P}(|Z^{(n)}| > \varepsilon) \le \mathbb{P}(|Z^{(n)}| > 0) \le \mathbb{P}(\Omega_n) \to 0$ as $n \to +\infty$, uniformly in $\varphi \in B\mathcal{O}$ (unconstrained). □

---

* See the calculation on p. 81 .

<u>Corollary</u>. (of the proof): If $(Y^{(n)})_{n\in\mathbb{N}} \subset \mathcal{SM}$ is such that $Y^{(n)}-Y^{(m)} = 0$ off $\overline{\mathbb{R}}_+\times\Omega_k$ for $m,n \geq k$, where $\mathbb{P}(\Omega_k) \to 0$ as $k \to \infty$, then $(Y^{(n)})_{n\in\mathbb{N}}$ is Cauchy, hence convergent in $\mathcal{SM}$.

There are several important subspaces of $\mathcal{SM}$. We denote by $\mathcal{V}_0$ the class of processes of finite variation, which vanish at time 0, furnished with the following complete metrizable topology: $V^{(n)} \to 0$ in $\mathcal{V}_0$ if $\int_{]0,+\infty]} |dV_s^{(n)}| \to 0$ in probability; and we pass from $\mathcal{V}_0$ to $\mathcal{V}$ as we did from $\mathcal{SM}_0$ to $\mathcal{SM}$. It is easy to see that we have a continuous inclusion of $\mathcal{V} \hookrightarrow \mathcal{SM}$. However, the topology of $\mathcal{V}$ is not the restriction of the topology of $\mathcal{SM}$; $\mathcal{V}$ is not a closed subset of $\mathcal{SM}$. It can be shown that this closure is all of $\widetilde{\mathcal{SM}}$, the class of characteristic components of semimartingales. Similarly the closure of $\mathcal{V} \cap \mathcal{M}L^2$ in $\mathcal{M}L^2$ is $\tilde{\mathcal{M}}L^2$ ($\mathcal{M}L^2 = \tilde{\mathcal{M}}L^2 \oplus \mathcal{M}^cL^2$), the space of purely discontinuous (square integrable) martingales.

There are two distinguished subspaces of $\mathcal{V}$ for which life is more pleasant, namely $\mathcal{V}^{pre}$ and $\mathcal{V}^c$, the predictable and continuous processes of finite variation, respectively. Clearly we have $\mathcal{V}^c \subset \mathcal{V}^{pre} \subset \mathcal{V} \hookrightarrow \mathcal{SM}$. Moreover it can be shown that $\mathcal{V}^c$ and $\mathcal{V}^{pre}$ are both closed subsets of $\mathcal{SM}$ and that they carry the induced topology. A similar situation arises for $\mathcal{M}^c$, the class of continuous local martingales. The closure of $\mathcal{M}$, the class of local martingales, in $\mathcal{SM}$ seems difficult to characterize.

We close this section by mentioning a few interesting continuous maps in connection with these topologies. The map $\mathcal{S}M \to (\widetilde{\mathcal{S}M}, \mathcal{M}^c)$ given by $X \mapsto (\tilde{X}, X^{(c)})$ is continuous so that $\mathcal{S}M = \widetilde{\mathcal{S}M} \oplus \mathcal{M}^c$. On the contrary, the special decomposition of local quasimartingales is not continuous. The brackets $\langle\cdot,\cdot\rangle : \mathcal{M}L^2_{loc} \times \mathcal{M}L^2_{loc} \to \mathcal{V}^{pre}$ and $[\cdot,\cdot] : \mathcal{S}M \times \mathcal{S}M \to \mathcal{V}$ are continuous bilinear maps.

CHAPTER 4

INTEGRABILITY; FORMAL MEASURES AND FORMAL SEMIMARTINGALES

1. INTEGRABILITY

We begin with a review of vector-valued integration, that is integration of real valued, not necessarily bounded, functions with respect to a vector-valued measure μ on a measurable space $(\Omega,\mathcal{O})$. In the case where μ takes its values in a Banach space E, recall that $f:\Omega \to \overline{\mathbb{R}}$ is said to be μ-integrable if there exists a sequence $(\varphi_n)_{n\in\mathbb{N}} \subset B\mathcal{O}$ such that $\mu^*(|f-\varphi_n|) \to 0$ as $n \to +\infty$ where for $f \in \mathcal{O}_+$ ($\overline{\mathbb{R}}_+$-valued):

$$\mu^*(f) = \sup\{\|\mu(\varphi)\|_E: \varphi \in B\mathcal{O}, \quad |\varphi| \leq f\},$$

and for general $f:\Omega \to \overline{\mathbb{R}}_+$:

$$\mu^*(f) = \inf\{\mu^*(g):g \in \mathcal{O}, \quad g \geq f\}.$$

In the case of interest to us, $E = L^0(\Omega,\mathcal{O},\mathbb{P})$ is not Banach and the definition is modified by replacing the single μ^* by a family of such, indexed by a family of neighbourhoods of $0 \in E$.

More precisely, if E is a complete metrizable topological vector space then there exists a fundamental system of neighbourhoods of its origin, consisting of balls with respect to a certain family of gauges $(|\cdot|_\alpha)_{\alpha>0}$ on E (a *gauge* on E is a non-negative homogeneous lower semicontinuous function $|\cdot|:E \to \bar{\mathbb{R}}_+$ which is also continuous at the origin; the ball of radius R with respect to this gauge is the set: $\{e \in E: |e| \le R\}$). For $f \in \mathcal{O}_+$ we define

$$\mu_\alpha^*(f) = \sup\{|\mu(\varphi)|_\alpha : \varphi \in B\mathcal{O},\ |\varphi| \le f\}$$

and for general $f:\Omega \to \bar{\mathbb{R}}_+$:

$$\mu_\alpha^*(f) = \inf\{\mu_\alpha^*(g) : g \in \mathcal{O},\ g \geqq f\}.$$

Again we say that a function is μ-*integrable* if there exists a sequence $(\varphi_n)_{n\in\mathbb{N}} \subset B\mathcal{O}$ such that $\mu_\alpha^*(|f-\varphi_n|) \to 0$ as $n \to +\infty$, for each $\alpha > 0$. This condition implies that the sequence $(\mu(\varphi_n))_{n\in\mathbb{N}}$ is Cauchy in E; the limit is independent of the approximating sequence $(\varphi_n)_{n\in\mathbb{N}}$ used, and is denoted by $\mu(f)$.

In the case $E = L^0(\Omega,\mathcal{O},\mathbb{P})$ we can use the family of gauges $(|\cdot|_\alpha)_{0<\alpha<1}$:

$$|f|_\alpha = \inf\{R \ge 0: \mathbb{P}\{|f| > R\} \le \alpha\}.$$

We can obtain the more classical notion of the completion of the measure μ (viewed as a countably additive set function) as follows. A set $A \subset \Omega$ is said to be *negligible* if $\mu_\alpha^*(A)=0$ for each α; the expression μ-a.e. refers to a statement valid except on a negligible set. We denote the class of negligible sets by $\mathcal{N}_\mu$. A set $A \subset \Omega$ which is the union of a set in $\mathcal{O}$ and a set in $\mathcal{N}_\mu$ is called μ-*measurable*, the class of such being $\hat{\mathcal{O}}^\mu = \mathcal{O} \vee \mathcal{N}_\mu$. Alternately, $A \subset \Omega$ is measurable if there are sets $B', B'' \in \mathcal{O}$ with $B' \subset A \subset B''$ and $B'' \setminus B' \in \mathcal{N}_\mu$. The extension of μ to $\hat{\mathcal{O}}_\mu$ is clear.

If $f:\Omega \to \overline{\mathbb{R}}$ is μ-integrable then so is $|f|$; also f is μ-measurable and $\mu_\alpha^*(|f|) < +\infty$ for each α. The converse is in general false but happens to be valid for a class of spaces which includes $L^0(\Omega,\mathcal{O},\mathbb{P})$, and for which a dominated convergence theorem holds: if $(f_n)_{n\in\mathbb{N}}$ are μ-measurable and converge μ-a.e. to f (necessarily μ-measurable) with $|f_n| \le g$ μ-a.e. where $\mu_\alpha^*(g) < +\infty$ for each α, then f is μ-integrable and $\mu(f_n) \to \mu(f)$ as $n \to +\infty$.

The use of an equivalent family of gauges would lead to the same notion of integrability as well as the resulting complete metrizable space $L^1(\Omega,\mathcal{O},\mu)$ (a fundamental system of neighbourhoods of $0 \in L^2(\Omega,\mathcal{O},\mu)$ is given by the family of balls with respect to the gauges $f \mapsto \mu_\alpha^*(f)$). It is therefore more natural (and useful) to have an equivalent description which doesn't make explicit mention of any particular family of gauges. We now summarize such a description.

A subset $A \subset \Omega$ is μ-negligible if it is contained in a μ-negligible set of $\mathcal{O}$, where a μ-negligible set of $\mathcal{O}$ is one whose every $\mathcal{O}$-measurable subset has μ-measure zero. Again $\hat{\mathcal{O}}_\mu = \mathcal{O} \vee \mathcal{N}_\mu$. A function $f:\mathfrak{R} \to \overline{\mathbb{R}}$ is μ-integrable if there exists a sequence $(\varphi_n)_{n\in\mathbb{N}} \subset B\mathcal{O}$ converging to f μ-a.e. such that $(\mu(\varphi_n\psi))_{n\in N}$ is Cauchy, uniformly in $\psi \in B\mathcal{O}$ with $\|\psi\|_\infty \leq 1$. This implies that the sequence $(\varphi_n)_{n\in\mathbb{N}}$ is Cauchy in L^1 and converges in L^1 necessarily to f i.e. $\mu(\varphi_n) \to \mu(f)$ as $n \to +\infty$. Similarly if $(f_n)_{n\in N} \subset L^1$ then $f_n \to 0$ means $\mu(f_n\varphi) \to 0$ uniformly in $\varphi \in B\mathcal{O}$ with $\|\varphi\|_\infty \leq 1$.

In the case $\mathfrak{R} = \overline{\mathbb{R}}_+\times\Omega$, $\mathcal{O}$ = Pre, $E = L^0(\Omega,\mathcal{O},\mathbb{P})$ one can show that f is μ_X-integrable, also called dX-integrable, (X a semimartingale) iff f is μ_X-measurable and there exists a decomposition $X = V+M$ such that $\int_{]0,+\infty]}|f_s||dV_s| < +\infty$ a.s. and $\int_{]0,+\infty]}|f_s|^2 d[M,M]_s < +\infty$ a.s. with $(f^2\cdot[M,M])^{1/2}$ locally integrable. At any rate the criterion we obtain from the general theory of integrability outlined above is that f must be μ_X-measurable and $(\mu_X)^*(|f|) < +\infty$
for each $0 < \alpha < 1$. For f predictable this is equivalent to the boundedness of $\{(\varphi\cdot X)_{+\infty}:\varphi \in B\text{Pre}, |\varphi| \leq f\}$ or equivalently $(f\cdot 1_{|f|\leq n})_{n\in N}$ in $L^0(\Omega,\mathcal{O},\mathbb{P})$.

Before returning to the general theory, we will discuss some simple but important instances of dX-negligibility and dX-integrability , in the form of two propositions.

<u>Proposition</u>. If $A \subset \overline{\mathbb{R}}_+\times\Omega$ is $\mathbb{P}$-negligible then A is dX-negligible for all $\mathbb{P}$-semimartingales X.

Proof. It suffices to consider the case $A \subset]0,+\infty]\times\Omega$. Define $T:\Omega \to \overline{\mathbb{R}}_+$ by

$$T(\omega) = \begin{cases} 0, & \text{if } A(\omega) \neq \phi \\ +\infty, & \text{if } A(\omega) = \phi \end{cases} .$$

Then $T = +\infty$ $\mathbb{P}$-a.e. which implies that T is a stopping time (recall that each $\mathcal{T}_t$ contains all $\mathbb{P}$-negligible subsets of $(\Omega,\mathcal{O})$). Since $A \subset]T,+\infty] \in \text{Pre}$, it suffices to show that $]T,+\infty]$ is dX-negligible, i.e. that every predictable subset of $]T,+\infty]$ has dX-measure zero. This is a consequence of localization (see (4) in the section on Theorems of Equivalence) applied to the compliment of $]T,+\infty]$ in $]0,+\infty]\times\Omega$. It can also be seen directly as follows. Clearly $\mu_X(]S_1,S_2]) = X_{S_2}-X_{S_1} = X_{+\infty}-X_{+\infty} = 0$ $\mathbb{P}$-a.e., for stopping times S_1,S_2 with $T \le S_1 \le S_2$. Therefore μ_X vanishes on the ring generated by such intervals. Now the collection N of predictable subsets of $]T,+\infty]$ with dX-measure zero is stable under complementation in $]T,+\infty]$ forms a monotone class, and contains a generating class for $\text{Pre} \cap]T,+\infty]$. By the monotone class theorem N contains, hence coincides with, $\text{Pre} \cap]T,+\infty]$. □

It is important to remember that although $\text{Pre} \subset \text{Opt}$, the dX-completion of Pre, $\widehat{\text{Pre}}^{\mu_X}$, contains sets not belonging to Opt, and $\text{Opt} \not\subset \widehat{\text{Pre}}^{\mu_X}$.

Definition. A process H is said to be *prelocally bounded* if there exist stopping times $(T_n)_{n\in\mathbb{N}}$, with $T_n \uparrow\uparrow \overline{+\infty}$, and numerical constants $(M_n)_{n\in\mathbb{N}}$ such that $|H| \le M_n$ in $[0,T_n[$ for each $n \in \mathbb{N}$. If $[0,T_n[$ can be replaced by $[0,T_n]$ then we say that H is *locally bounded;* this is certainly the case if H is left continuous, prelocally bounded and $H_0=0$. We say that $(M_n,T_n)_{n\in\mathbb{N}}$ (pre) locally bound H.

Note that for $H \in \mathrm{Opt}$, H is prelocally bounded iff each trajectory $H(\omega)$ is bounded.

Proposition. If H is predictable and prelocally bounded then H is dX-integrable.

Proof. We must find a sequence $(H^{(n)})_{n\in\mathbb{N}} \subset \mathrm{BPre}$ such that $H^{(n)} \to H$ pointwise as $n \to +\infty$ and $(\mu_X(H^{(n)}))_{n\in\mathbb{N}}$ is Cauchy in $L^0(\Omega,\mathcal{O},\mathbb{P})$. Take $H^{(n)} = H\cdot 1_{\{|H|\le M_n\}}$ where $(M_n,T_n)_{n\in\mathbb{N}}$ prelocally bound H. (Note that $H\cdot 1_{[0,T_n[}$ would not be suitable as $[0,T_n[$ is not predictable.) For $m,n \ge k$, $H^{(n)}-H^{(m)} = 0$ on $[0,T_k[\supset \overline{\mathbb{R}}_+\times\{T_k=\overline{+\infty}\}=\Omega_k$. By localization, $\mu_X(H^{(n)}-H^{(m)})$ vanishes off $\{T_k < \overline{+\infty}\}$, and $\mathbb{P}\{T_k < \overline{+\infty}\} \to 0$ as $k \to +\infty$. Therefore, given $\varepsilon > 0$:

$$\begin{aligned}\mathbb{P}(|\mu_X(H^{(n)})-\mu_X(H^{(m)})| > \varepsilon) &\le \mathbb{P}(|\mu_X(H^{(n)}-H^{(m)})| > 0)\\ &\le \mathbb{P}(\Omega_k) \text{ for } m,n \ge k\\ &\to 0 \quad \text{as} \quad k \to +\infty.\end{aligned}$$

(We could also have proceeded equivalently by showing that $(H^{(n)}\cdot X)_{n\in\mathbb{N}}$ is Cauchy in $\mathcal{SM}_0$, using the corollary to the lemma in the section on semimartingale topologies, to conclude the existence of $H\cdot X$.) □

Returning to the general theory, the intrinsic description of the topology of $L^1(\mathfrak{R},\mathfrak{O},\mu)$ can be better understood via its embedding $\mathrm{Meas}(\mathfrak{R},\mathfrak{O},E)$ effected by the following operation of *multiplication*. If $f \in B\mathfrak{O}$, or more generally μ-integrable, we can form a new measure $f\mu$ where $f\mu(\varphi) = \mu(f\varphi)$ for $\varphi \in B\mathfrak{O}$. We have topologized $L^1(\mathfrak{R},\mathfrak{O},\mu)$ so that the mapping $\tilde{\mu}: L^1 \to \mathrm{Meas}$ given by $f \mapsto f\mu$ is an embedding. Thus we have the following schematic summary of the intrinsic description of the topology on $L^1(\mathfrak{R},\mathfrak{O},\mu)$:

$$L^1(\mathfrak{R},\mathfrak{O},\mu) \simeq L^1(\mathfrak{R},\mathfrak{O},\mu)\mu \subset \mathrm{Meas}(\mathfrak{R},\mathfrak{O},E) \subset \mathcal{L}(B\mathfrak{O},E);$$

$L^1(\mathfrak{R},\mathfrak{O},\mu)\mu$ is the closure in $\mathrm{Meas}(\mathfrak{R},\mathfrak{O},E)$ of $(B\mathfrak{O})\mu$. The map $\tilde{\mu}: L^1 \to \mathrm{Meas}$ restricted to $B\mathfrak{O}$ is also a vector-valued measure with values in $\mathrm{Meas}(\mathfrak{R},\mathfrak{O},E)$; f is $\tilde{\mu}$-integrable iff f is μ-integrable and of course $\tilde{\mu}(f) = f\mu$.

In the case $\mathfrak{R} = \overline{\mathbb{R}}_+\times\Omega$, $\mathfrak{O} = \mathrm{Pre}$, $E = L^0(\mathfrak{R},\mathfrak{O},\mathbb{P})$ the equivalence of μ_X- and $\tilde{\mu}_X$-integrability is just the simultaneous existence or non-existence of $\int_{]0,+\infty]} f_s dX_s$ and $f\cdot X$: for $\varphi,\psi \in B\mathrm{Pre}$

$$\tilde{\mu}_X(\psi)(\varphi) = \psi\mu_X(\varphi) = \mu_X(\psi\varphi) = ((\psi\varphi)\cdot X)_{+\infty}$$

$$= (\varphi\cdot(\psi\cdot X))_{+\infty} = \mu_{\psi\cdot X}(\varphi) ;$$

that is $\tilde{\mu}_X(\psi) = \mu_{\psi\cdot X}$, or the range of $\tilde{\mu}_X|_{B\mathfrak{O}}$ is contained in $\mathcal{SM} \subset \mathrm{Meas}$. By the dominated convergence theorem and the closedness of $\mathcal{SM}$ we obtain that the range of $\tilde{\mu}_X$ is contained in $\mathcal{SM}$. As a byproduct of the calculation above, we obtain that for $\psi \in$ BPre: $\psi\mu_X = \mu_{\psi \cdot X}$.

At this point it is appropriate to define the stochastic integral $f \cdot X$ for f μ_X-integrable. If $f_n \to f$ in $L^1(\mu_X)$ with f_n bounded then $f_n\mu_X \to f\mu$ in Meas, therefore $(f_n \cdot X)_{n \in \mathbb{N}}$ is a Cauchy sequence in $\mathcal{SM}_0$ which is complete. Therefore we have a limit $Y \in \mathcal{SM}_0$, and $\mu_Y = f\mu_X$. Now $f \cdot X$ has only one reasonable definition: Y (it is easy to see that it does not depend on the choice of $(f_n)_{n \in \mathbb{N}}$). Since $f_n 1_{]0,t]} \to f 1_{]0,t]}$ in $L^1(\mu_X)$, $\mu_X(f_n 1_{]0,t]}) = (f_n \cdot X)_t$ converges to both $\mu_X(f 1_{]0,t]})$ and Y_t in L^0. Thus for each $t \in \mathbb{R}_+$ $\mu_X(f 1_{]0,t]}) = Y_t$ $\mathbb{P}$-a.e. . In other words we have in $f \cdot X := Y$, a semimartingale which is a cadlag version of $\mu_X(f 1_{]0,\cdot]})$; and $\mu_{f \cdot X} = f\mu_X$, extending the result of the previous paragraph.

A general property of this operation of multiplication is that if g is μ-integrable then fg is μ-integrable iff f is $g\mu$-integrable, in which case $f(g\mu) = (fg)\mu$. (A remedy for the awkwardness of this statement will be presented in the discussion on formal measures.) Combining this with the result of the previous paragraph we obtain that if g is dX-integrable (X is semimartingale) then f is $d(g \cdot X)$-integrable iff fg is dX-integrable, in which case $f \cdot (g \cdot X) = (fg) \cdot X$.

We can rephrase the integrability criterion for $f \in$ Pre as the boundedness of $\{\varphi \cdot X : \varphi \in \text{BPre}, |\varphi| \leq f\}$ in $\mathcal{SM}$.

2. FORMAL MEASURES

In order to motivate the notion of formal measure consider the following simple situation. Suppose f is a real-valued Borel function, on some finite interval $]a,b]$, which is not Lebesgue integrable on any subinterval. Then it has no primitive (or cumulative distribution function) but if f is nonnegative one can still give a sense to f(x)dx in two ways. The first and traditional is to consider it as a nonnegative "measure", $A \mapsto \int_A f(x)dx$, which admits the value $+\infty$. Under the convention $r+\infty = +\infty+r = +\infty$ for $r \in \mathbb{R}_+$, trouble never arises; but not so if f is signed. The second way is to realize that f(x)dx defined in the previous fashion is σ-finite: $]a,b] = \bigcup_{k\in\mathbb{N}} \{|f| \le k\}$ and on each of the sets $\Omega_k = \{|f| \le k\}$, f(x)dx is a (finite) measure, say μ_k, and the collection $\{(\mu_k,\Omega_k)\}_{k\in\mathbb{N}}$ suffices to describe f(x)dx on $]a,b]$. However, if f is signed the collection $\{(\mu_k,\Omega_k)\}_{k\in\mathbb{N}}$ is still defined and we can define f(x)dx to be this collection which behaves like an inductive system: $\Omega_k \subset \Omega_{k+1}$, $\bigcup_{k\in\mathbb{N}} \Omega_k =]a,b]$, $\mu_{k+1}|_{\Omega_k} = \mu_k$. Modulo the slight technicality that the correspondance is not one-one this turns out to be the fruitful generalization.

A *formal measure* μ on a measurable space $(\Omega,\mathcal{O})$ with values in a complete metrizable topological vector space E is defined to be an equivalence class of collections $\{(\mu_k, \mathcal{R}_k)\}_{k\in\mathbb{N}}$ where $(\mathcal{R}_k)_{k\in\mathbb{N}}$ is an increasing sequence of members of $\mathcal{O}$ with union $\mathcal{R}$ and $\mu_k \in \mathrm{Meas}(\mathcal{R}_k, \mathcal{O}\cap\mathcal{R}_k, E)$ such that $\mu_{k+1}|_{\mathcal{R}_k} = \mu_k$; two collections $\{(\mu_k, \mathcal{R}_k)\}_{k\in\mathbb{N}}$ and $\{(\mu'_k, \mathcal{R}'_k)\}_{k\in\mathbb{N}}$ being equivalent if $\mu_k|_{\mathcal{R}_k\cap\mathcal{R}'_k} = \mu'_k|_{\mathcal{R}_k\cap\mathcal{R}'_k}$. Given a family of gauges $(|\cdot|_\alpha)_{\alpha>0}$ defining the topology of E, we set for $f \in \mathcal{O}$

$$\mu^*_\alpha(f) = \sup\{|\mu_k(\varphi|_{\mathcal{R}_k})|_\alpha : \varphi \in B\mathcal{O},\ |\varphi| \le f,\ k \in \mathbb{N}\}$$

and the notions of integrability, L^1, etc. follow suit in much the same way as for true measures. We shall not dwell upon the details but note that whatever was independent of the choice of gauges for measures, remains so for formal measures. A formal measure is a measure, that is $\mu_k = \mu|_{\mathcal{R}_k}$ for some measure $\mu \in \mathrm{Meas}(\mathcal{R}, \mathcal{O}, E)$ and every representative $\{(\mu_k, \mathcal{R}_k)\}_{k\in\mathbb{N}}$, iff the constant 1 is integrable i.e. $\mu^*_\alpha(\mathcal{R}^c_k) \to 0$ as $k \to +\infty$ for each α.

Of utmost importance is the extension of the operation of multiplication. If μ is a formal measure represented by $\{(\mu_k, \mathcal{R}_k)\}_{k\in\mathbb{N}}$ and h is a μ-measurable real-valued function, then $h\mu$ is the formal measure containing the representative $\{(h\mu_k, \mathcal{R}_k\cap\{|h|\le k\})\}_{k\in\mathbb{N}}$. Note that f is $h\mu$-integrable iff fh is μ-integrable. In particular, h is μ-integrable iff 1 is $h\mu$-integrable, i.e. iff $h\mu$ is a measure. It is not hard to see that every formal measure μ admits a positive $\mathcal{O}$-measurable and integrable function γ. In other words $\gamma\mu$ is a true measure and it is easy to check that $\mu = (1/\gamma)(\gamma\mu)$. Thus a good notation for the class of E-valued formal measures is $\mathcal{O}$Meas$(\Omega,\mathcal{O},E)$, indicating that they are precisely the products of elements of $\mathcal{O}$ with elements of Meas$(\Omega,\mathcal{O},E)$.

It might seem that the definition of a formal measure is quite reminiscent of the classical description of a tensor in algebra; indeed the analogy is more than superficial. The vector space $\mathcal{O}$Meas$(\Omega,\mathcal{O},E)$ is clearly closed under multiplication by $\mathcal{O}$ and moreover if $\mu \in \mathcal{O}$Meas and $f,g \in \mathcal{O}$ then $f(g\mu) = (fg)\mu$ — note the simplicity of this statement as compared with that in the case of true measures. Thus $\mathcal{O}$Meas is a $\mathcal{O}$-module ($\mathcal{O}$ being a ring with the usual pointwise definition of addition and multiplication); but $\mathcal{O}$ and Meas are clearly also $B\mathcal{O}$-modules, so that $\mathcal{O}$Meas has been constructed, in the language of algebra, as an extension of the $B\mathcal{O}$-module Meas by an extension of the base ring $B\mathcal{O} \to \mathcal{O}$ i.e. $\mathcal{O}\text{Meas} \cong \mathcal{O}\otimes_{B\mathcal{O}}\text{Meas}$. The isomorphism is given by $h\otimes\mu \mapsto h\mu$. (It might be helpful to recall that to complexify a vector space V, over the reals, in a coordinate-free manner, one can simply form $\mathbb{C}\otimes_{\mathbb{R}} V$.)

The utility of $\mathcal{O}$Meas lies in the unconditional equality $f(g\mu) = (fg)\mu$ and the possibility of "integrating" to one's heart's content. Problems with integrability in various calculations might be avoided by dealing with the well defined object $f\mu$ instead of $\mu(f)$ which might not have a sense. For example, if the first and last lines of a "formal" calculation involve measures and integrable functions but perhaps not in between, the derivation might be made rigorous by switching from $\mu(f)$ to $f\mu$ everywhere. Another important application in the same vein comes in noting that a difference of two formal measures might very well be a true measure. Formal measures can play a role in integration analogous to that of distributions (generalized functions) in differentiation (e.g. partial differential equations).

Concerning the topology of $\mathcal{O}$Meas, we say that $(\mu_n)_{n\in\mathbb{N}} \subset \mathcal{O}$Meas converges to $\mu \in \mathcal{O}$Meas if there is a positive $\gamma \in B\mathcal{O}$ such that $(\gamma\mu_n)_{n\in\mathbb{N}}$ converges to $\gamma\mu$ in Meas. It is easy to check that this notion of limit is well defined. If $(h_n)_{n\in\mathbb{N}} \subset \mathcal{O}$ converges pointwise to h and $(\mu_n)_{n\in\mathbb{N}} \subset \mathcal{O}$Meas converges to $\mu \in \mathcal{O}$Meas then $(h_n\mu_n)_{n\in\mathbb{N}}$ converges to $h\mu$ in $\mathcal{O}$Meas. If $(h_n\mu)_{n\in\mathbb{N}} \subset \mathcal{O}$Meas converges to 0 then there is a subsequence of $(h_n)_{n\in\mathbb{N}}$ which tends to 0 μ-a.e. .

3. FORMAL SEMIMARTINGALES

Turning to probabilistic matters, we have seen that $\mathcal{SM}$ is a BPre-submodule of Meas$(\bar{\mathbb{R}}_+\times\Omega,\text{Pre},L^0(\Omega,\mathcal{O},\mathbb{P}))$; moreover if

$X \in \mathcal{SM}$ and f is dX-integrable then $f\cdot X \in \mathcal{SM}$ ($f\mu_X = \mu_{f\cdot X}$ is adapted and localizable). Interpreting the notions developed so far concerning formal measures, in the case $\mathfrak{R} = \bar{\mathbb{R}}_+\times\Omega$, $\mathfrak{O} = \text{Pre}$, $E = L^0(\Omega,\mathcal{O},\mathbb{P})$ we are led to the submodule Pre$\mathcal{SM}$ of PreMeas, which is the class of *formal semimartingales*. A formal semimartingale will occasionally be denoted by X or dX or μ_X, though strictly speaking there is not necessarily a process (primitive) X in existence. Continuing the abuse of notation, if f is dX-integrable, we shall write $f\mu_X = \mu_{f\cdot X}$. A characterization of Pre$\mathcal{SM}$ within PreMeas is as follows: a formal L^0-valued measure μ is a formal semimartingale iff it is adapted and localizable. Adapted here means that if f is μ-integrable and supported in $]0,t]\times\Omega$ then $\mu(f) \in \mathcal{T}_t$; localizable means that if f is μ-integrable and supported in $]0,+\infty]\times\Omega'$, $\Omega' \in \Omega$, then $\text{supp}\,\mu(f) \subset \Omega'$. Also $\mu \in \text{Pre}\mathcal{SM}$ iff there exists a (strictly) positive $\gamma \in \text{BPre}$ such that $\gamma\mu \in \mathcal{SM}$; in which case we would write $\gamma\mu = \gamma\cdot X \in \mathcal{SM}$ if $\mu = X \in \text{Pre}\,\mathcal{SM}$ (this summarizes well the various abuses of notation introduced above).

Much of the theory of stochastic processes and integration carries over to the class of formal semimartingales. For instance, we still have a decomposition $\text{Pre}\mathcal{SM} = \text{Pre}\mathcal{V} \oplus \text{Pre}\mathcal{M}^c$ (with sequential continuity of the component map $\text{Pre}\mathcal{SM} \to \text{Pre}\mathcal{V} \oplus \text{Pre}\mathcal{M}^c$ given by $X \mapsto (\tilde{X}, X^{(c)})$. A sense can be given to stopping a formal semimartingale. Recall that for a stopping time T and a semimartingale X, $X^T = 1_{]0,T]} \cdot X$; so it is natural to define X^T, for a formal semimartingale X, by $1_{]0,T]}\mu_X$ (which by convention still reads as $\mu_{(1_{]0,T]} \cdot X)}$ or $1_{]0,T]} \circ X$). It is easy to see that $X \mapsto X^T$ is a sequentially continuous (Pre-linear) endomorphism of $\mathrm{Pre}\mathcal{SM}$ with image $\mathrm{Pre}\mathcal{SM}^T$. We can also define the jumps ΔX_s of a formal semimartingale to be the process $\Delta X_s := \frac{1}{\gamma_s} \Delta(\gamma \cdot X)_s$ where $\gamma \in$ BPre is positive and dX-integrable. If γ' is another such candidate then

$$\begin{aligned}\gamma'\Delta(\gamma\cdot X) &= \Delta(\gamma'\cdot(\gamma\cdot X)) = \Delta((\gamma'\gamma)\cdot X)\\ &= \Delta(\gamma\cdot(\gamma'\cdot X)) = \gamma\Delta(\gamma'\cdot X)\end{aligned}$$

so that our definition is independent of the choice of γ. Choosing an increasing sequence $(A_k)_{k \in \mathbb{N}}$ of elements of Pre whose union is $\bar{\mathbb{R}}_+ \times \Omega$, such that each A_k is dX-integrable we can say that $\sum_{s \in A_k(w)} (\Delta X_s(w))^2 < +\infty$ for each $k \in \mathbb{N}$ $\mathbb{P}$-a.e. . Also for $\gamma \in$ Pre and dX-integrable, $\sum_s \gamma_s^2 (\Delta X_s)^2 < +\infty$ $\mathbb{P}$-a.e. . If $\Delta X = 0$ then we say that X is continuous. Finally we can define a Pre-bilinear sequentially continuous map $[\cdot,\cdot]$: $\mathrm{Pre}\mathcal{SM} \cdot \mathrm{Pre}\mathcal{SM} \to \mathrm{Pre}\mathcal{V}$ given by $[X,Y] = \frac{1}{\gamma^2} \cdot [\gamma \cdot X, \gamma \cdot Y]$ where $\gamma \in$ BPre is positive and dX- and dY-integrable. It is easy to check that this definition is independent of the choice of γ . Interpreted appropriately,

$$[X,Y] = \sum_{0<s\leq \cdot} \Delta X_s \Delta Y_s + \langle X^{(c)}, Y^{(c)} \rangle$$

again, for $X,Y \in \mathrm{Pre}\mathcal{SM}_0$.

We conclude with a theoretical application of these ideas. If X is a semimartingale with values in a finite dimensional real vector space E, with dual E*, and J is an E*-valued predictable process then when should we say that J is dX-integrable? In terms of coordinates with respect to some basis $E \cong \mathbb{R}^n$ and $J_k \cdot X_k$ always exists as a formal semimartingale for each $k=1,2,\ldots,n$. If the formal semimartingale $\sum_{k=1}^{n} J_k \cdot X_k$ is actually a true semimartingale then we say that J is dX-integrable (it is easy to see that this definition is independent of the basis chosen) and denote the integrated process by $\int_{]0,t]} (J_s | dX_s)_{E,E^*}$.

CHAPTER 5

THEOREMS OF EQUIVALENCE

The material of this section is fundamental for an understanding of stochastic "differentials" and integration on a manifold; in particular for the local description of a stochastic differential equation on a manifold. It also deals with the deferred proof of the localizability of μ_X for $X \in \mathcal{SM}$. We begin with a definition.

If A is an open subset of $\bar{\mathbb{R}}_+ \times \Omega$ and X,Y two vector valued functions on A, we say that X is *equivalent to* Y *on* A, written $X \underset{A}{\sim} Y$, if X-Y is locally constant on almost every section $A(\omega)$.

In the following five theorems which concern topological localization (as opposed to the type to be discussed in the section on the localization principle, A will be an open subset of $\bar{\mathbb{R}}_+ \times \Omega$ and all processes will be defined globally.

Theorem 1. If $M \in \mathcal{ML}^2_{loc}$ and $\langle M,M\rangle \underset{A}{\sim} 0$ then $M \underset{A}{\sim} 0$.

Theorem 2. If $X,Y \in \mathcal{SM}$ and $X \underset{A}{\sim} 0$ then $[X,Y] \underset{A}{\sim} 0$.

Theorem 3. If $X \in \mathcal{SM}$ and $X \underset{A}{\sim} 0$ then $X^{(c)}, X \underset{A}{\sim} 0$.

Theorem 4. If $X \in \mathcal{SM}$, H is dX-integrable and either $H \in \text{Pre}$ with $H = 0$ on $A\backslash\{0\}\times\Omega$, or $X \underset{A}{\sim} 0$ then $H\cdot X \underset{A}{\sim} 0$. In particular μ_X is localizable.

Theorem 5. If $A = \bigcup_{n\in N} A_n$ with $X \underset{A_n}{\sim} M_n \in \mathcal{M}^c_{loc}$ then $X \underset{A}{\sim} X^{(c)}$, i.e. if $X \underset{A_n}{\sim}$ continuous local martingale then $X \underset{A}{\sim}$ continuous local martingale.

Before giving proofs of these statements we point out that in the absence of continuity, the converse of (1) is false (when M is continuous the converse is supplied by (2) since in this case $\langle M,M\rangle = [M,M]$). To see this consider the following counterexample. We let $\Omega = \{\omega_1,\omega_2,\omega_3\}$ with $\mathcal{F}$ = all subsets of Ω, $\mathbb{P}(\omega_i) = 1/3$, $i=1,2,3$, $\mathcal{F}_t = \{\phi,\Omega\}$ for $t \in \mathbb{R}_+$ and $\mathcal{F}_{+\infty} = \mathcal{F}$. Define the martingale M by $M_t = 0$ for $t \in \mathbb{R}_+$ and $M_{+\infty}(\omega_i) = \begin{cases} 1, & i=1 \\ 0, & i=2 \\ -1, & i=3 \end{cases}$. Then graphically:

	M			M^2			$\langle M,M\rangle$			$M^2-\langle M,M\rangle$		
$t=+\infty$	1	0	-1	1	0	1	$\frac{2}{3}$	$\frac{2}{3}$	$\frac{2}{3}$	$\frac{1}{3}$	$-\frac{2}{3}$	$\frac{1}{3}$
$t=0$	0	0	0	0	0	0	0	0	0	0	0	0
	ω_1	ω_2	ω_3	ω_1	ω_2	ω_3	ω_1	ω_2	ω_3	ω_1	ω_2	ω_3

To see that $\langle M,M\rangle$ is as indicated it suffices to observe that the table depicts an increasing cadlag predictable process (it is $\frac{2}{3}1_{\{+\infty\}\times\Omega}$ and $\{+\infty\}\times\Omega = \bigcap_{n\in N}]n,+\infty]\times\Omega$) whose difference from M^2 (in the next table) is clearly a martingale. However $M(\omega_2) = 0$ while $\langle M,M\rangle_{+\infty}(\omega_2) \neq 0$ so that $M \underset{A}{\sim} 0$ while $\langle M,M\rangle \underset{A}{\not\sim} 0$ on $A = \mathbb{R}_+\times\{\omega_2\}$.

We also mention that (3) is false for the components of the special decomposition of a special semimartingale. The special case $M \underset{A}{\sim} 0$ iff $\langle M,M\rangle \underset{A}{\sim} 0$ for $M \in \mathcal{M}^c$ is originally due to Sharpe.

<u>Proofs of (1)-(5).</u> (1) Since $\langle M^T,M^T\rangle = \langle M,M\rangle^T$ for T a stopping time, it suffices to verify this proposition for $M \in L^2$. In this case, for each $s \in \mathbb{Q}_+$ we define the stopping time $S_s = \inf\{t\geq s: \langle M,M\rangle_t - \langle M,M\rangle_{s-} \neq 0\}$ so that $A \subset \bigcup_{s\in\mathbb{Q}_+} [s,S_s[^\circ$ (by convention $0^- = 0$); it suffices to show that M is constant on almost every section of each $[s,S_s[^\circ$.

Define as well auxiliary stopping times $S_n \geq S$ (we suppress the dependence on s as it will be fixed momentarily) by $S_n = \inf\{t \geq s: \langle M,M\rangle_t - \langle M,M\rangle_{s-} \geq \frac{1}{n}\}$. A theorem of Dellacherie (T predictable iff T announcible) implies that the beginning, or first entrance time D_A (in our case S_n) of a predictable set A containing its beginning when not $\overline{+\infty}$ (in our case $\{t \geq s: \langle M,M\rangle_t - \langle M,M\rangle_{s-} \geq 1/n\}$) is an announcible stopping time. Note that D_A being predictable is simple to prove: D_A is a stopping time and the graph of $D_A = [D_A] = A\setminus]D_A,+\infty] \in$ Pre.

Note that on $[s,+\infty]\times\Omega$, $\langle M-M_s, M-M_s\rangle = \langle M,M\rangle - \langle M,M\rangle_s$ for each $s \geq 0$ (this "s" is independent of the one in the previous paragraph), since the right hand side is clearly cadlag increasing and predictable, and

$$(M-M_s)^2 - \langle M,M\rangle + \langle M,M\rangle_s = [M^2 - \langle M,M\rangle] + [-2M_s M + M_s^2 + \langle M,M\rangle_s]$$

is evidently the sum of two mean zero martingales. Therefore if $T \geq s$ is a stopping time

$$E[M_T - M_s]^2 = E[\langle M,M\rangle_T - \langle M,M\rangle_s].$$

If $s \geq 0$ and $T_k \geq s_k$ with $T_k \uparrow T$, $T_k < T$ on $\{T>s\}$, and $s_k \uparrow s$, $s_k < s$ if $s > 0$ ($s_k=0$ if $s=0$), then applying Fatou's lemma to the left hand side and Lebesgue's dominated convergence theorem to the right hand side of this equality with T_k, s_k in the roles of T,s, we obtain

$$E[M_{T^-}-M_{s^-}]^2 \le E[\langle M,M\rangle_{T^-}-\langle M,M\rangle_{s^-}]$$

($0^- \equiv 0$, again).

Applying this inequality to $T = (S_n \wedge t)$ and the corresponding s upon which S_n depends, for $t > s$, we have the following estimate

$$E[M_{(S_n\wedge t)^-}-M_{s^-}]^2 = E[\langle M,M\rangle_{(S_n\wedge t)^-}-\langle M,M\rangle_{s^-}] \le \frac{1}{n}.$$

Letting $n \to +\infty$ and applying Fatou's lemma once more yields $\liminf_{n\to+\infty} [M_{(S_n\wedge t)^-}-M_{s^-}]^2 = 0$ almost surely; but on the set $\{s < t < S\}$, $S_n \wedge t = t$ so that $M_{t^-} = M_{s^-}$ for $(t,\omega) \in]s,S[$. As M is right continuous we conclude that $M_t = M_{s^-}$ on $[s,S[^\circ$ almost surely. □

(2) $[X,Y]_t = \lim_{n\to+\infty} \sum_{i=0}^{n-1} (X_{t^n_{i+1}\wedge t} - X_{t^n_i\wedge t})(Y_{t^n_{i+1}\wedge t} - Y_{t^n_i\wedge t})$ $+ X_0Y_0$, where the limit is in probability uniformly in t as $\max_{0\le i\le n-2} (t^n_{i+1}-t^n_i) \to 0$ and $t^n_{n-1} \to +\infty$ as $n \to +\infty$, $(t^n_i)^n_{i=0}$ being a partition of $\bar{\mathbb{R}}_+$. Choose a sequence of partitions such that we have almost sure convergence. If $X(\omega)$ is constant on some interval $]a,b[\subset A(\omega)$ then each term of the sum remains constant in t when t varies in $[0,t^n_i]$ and in $[t^n_{i+1},+\infty]$; and in $[t^n_i,t^n_{i+1}]$ if $a < t^n_i < t^n_{i+1} < b$. Therefore if i_n is the first index such that $t^n_{i_n} > a$ and

j_n is the last index such that $t^n_{j_n+1} < b$, then for sufficiently large $n = n(\omega)$, i_n and j_n are well defined with $i_n<j_n$, and the total sum does not vary with t at all for $t^n_{i_n} \le t \le t^n_{j_n+1}$, as $[t^n_{i_n}, t^n_{j_n+1}]$ is a common interval of constancy for each term. Since $t^n_{i_n} \to 0$ and $t^n_{j_n+1} \to b$ as $n \to +\infty$ $[X,Y](\omega)$ does not vary with t for $a < t < b$. □

(3) By the alternate expression for [X,X] we can write

$$<X^{(c)}, X^{(c)}>_t = [X,X]_t - X_0 - \sum_{0<s\le t} \Delta X_s \text{ .}$$

If $X \underset{A}{\sim} 0$ then by (2), $[X,X] \underset{A}{\sim} 0$ and clearly $\sum_{0\le s\le \cdot} (\Delta X_s)^2 \underset{A}{\sim} 0$, so that $<X^{(c)}, X^{(c)}> \underset{A}{\sim} 0$. By (1) we conclude that $X^{(c)} \underset{A}{\sim} 0$, and therefore $\tilde{X} = X - X^{(c)} \underset{A}{\sim} 0$. The converse is trivial. □

(4) In order to avoid repetition, we begin with the observation that if H is dX-integrable and $(H_{(n)})_{n\in N} \subset$ BPre, with $H_{(n)} \to H$ μ_X-a.e., $(H_{(n)}\cdot X)_{n\in N}$ Cauchy in $\mathcal{SM}$, and such that each $H_{(n)}\cdot X \underset{A}{\sim} 0$, then $H\cdot X \underset{A}{\sim} 0$. Indeed, $(H_{(n)}\cdot X)_{n\in N}$ is Cauchy in Cadlag so there exists a subsequence $(H_{(n_k)}\cdot X)_{k\in N}$ converging uniformly in t $\mathbb{P}$-a.e.. Hence $H\cdot X = \lim_{k\to+\infty} (H_{(n_k)}\cdot X) \underset{A}{\sim} 0$. We handle the alternate hypotheses separately.

(i) If $X \underset{A}{\sim} 0$ then clearly $c1_{]S,T]} \cdot X(\omega) = c(\omega)[X^T(\omega) - X^S(\omega)]$ $(c \in \mathcal{T}_S)$ is constant wherever X is, so for H of the form $\sum_{i=1}^{n} c_i 1_{]S_i,T_i]}$ with $c_i \in \mathcal{T}_{S_i}$ (these generate BPre) we have $H \cdot X \underset{A}{\sim} 0$. Combining the observation above with the functional form of the Monotone Class theorem yields $H \cdot X \underset{A}{\sim} 0$ for all $H \in$ BPre. Using the definition of dX-integrability and applying the observation once more yields the result for H dX-integrable.

(ii) Let $H \in$ Pre with H = 0 on $A \backslash \{0\} \times \Omega$, and suppose firstly that H is bounded. Decompose $X = V + M$ with $M \in \mathcal{M}L^2_{loc}$. Clearly $H \cdot V(t,\omega) = \int_{]0,t]} H_s(\omega) dV_s(\omega) = \int_{]0,a]} H_s(\omega) dV_s(\omega)$ for $t \in]a,b[$, if $H_s(\omega) = 0$ for $s \in]a,b[$, so that $H \cdot V \underset{A}{\sim} 0$. The general case H dX-integrable follows from the observation applied to $H_{(n)} := H1_{\{|H| \leq n\}}$.

Applying part (ii) to an $H \in$ BPre with H = 0 on $A = \bar{\mathbb{R}}_+ \times \Omega_0$, $\Omega_0 \subset \Omega$, yields the localizability of μ_X. □

(5) If $X \underset{A_n}{\sim} M_{(n)} \in \mathcal{M}^c_{loc}$ then $0 \underset{A_n}{\sim} X - M_{(n)}$ implies $0 \underset{A_n}{\sim} \widetilde{X - M_{(n)}} = \tilde{X} - \tilde{M}_{(n)} = \tilde{X}$, by (3). Thus $\tilde{X} \underset{A}{\sim} 0$, or $X - X^{(c)} \underset{A}{\sim} 0$. □

Some simple extensions of these results may be obtained by suitable replacements of 0 in the equivalences. For instance, regarding (2): if $X,X',Y,Y' \in \mathcal{SM}$ and $X \underset{A}{\sim} X'$, $Y \underset{A}{\sim} Y'$ then $[X,Y] \underset{A}{\sim} [X',Y']$ follows from the identity $[X,Y]-[X',Y'] = [X-X',Y]+[X',Y-Y']$ and (2). Regarding (4), if $X,X' \in \mathcal{SM}$, H,H' both dX- and dX'-integrable and $H = H'$ on $A\setminus\{0\}\times\Omega$, $X \underset{A}{\sim} X'$, then $H\cdot X \underset{A}{\sim} H'\cdot X'$ follows from the identity $H\cdot X-H'\cdot X = (H-H')\cdot X+H'\cdot(X-X')$ and (4).

We can extend the notion of equivalence to formal semimartingales as follows. If $X \in \text{Pre}\,\mathcal{SM}$ and $A \subset \bar{\mathbb{R}}_+\times\Omega$ is open then we say $X \underset{A}{\sim} 0$ if for some (hence all) strictly positive dX-integrable $\gamma \in \text{BPre}$, $\gamma.X \underset{A}{\sim} 0$. Theorems (1)-(5) extend immediately to this setting.

If $X \in \mathcal{SM}^c$ then theorem (4) is valid for $H \in \text{Opt}$ since the original proof still works if only $H = 0$ on $A\setminus\{0\}\times\Omega$ except possibly on a set having denumerable sections. Thus the equivalences are also valid for $X \in \text{Opt}\mathcal{SM}^c$ as well.

CHAPTER 6

ITO'S FORMULA

In this section we embark on the development of a calculus for semimartingales, with an analogue of the fundamental theorem of calculus, namely Itô's formula.

Let X be a semimartingale with values in a finite dimensional real vector space E, say $\mathbb{R}^d$ through the introduction of coordinates with respect to some basis (it is easy to see that the property of being a semimartingale is independent of the basis chosen), and let $\Phi \in C^2(\mathbb{R}^d, \mathbb{R})$. Beginning with the case d=1 and proceeding naively to expand $\Phi(X_t)$ into a Taylor series up to a second order, we are led to the expression:

$$\Phi(X_{t+dt}) - \Phi(X_t) = \Phi'(X_t)dX_t + \frac{1}{2}\Phi''(X_t)(dX_t)^2.$$

The reason for retaining the quadratic infinitesimal term $(dX_t)^2$ is that in general the quadratic variation $[X,X]_t - X_0^2 = \lim \sum_i (X_{t_{i+1}\wedge t} - X_{t_i \wedge t})^2$ is not zero.

More rigorously if one applies Taylor's theorem properly then one obtains after a long calculation, which will not be carried out here, the celebrated Itô Formula:

$$\Phi(X_t)-\Phi(X_0) = \int_{]0,t]} \Phi'(X_{s-})dX_s + \frac{1}{2}\int_{]0,t]} \Phi''(X_{s-})d\langle X^{(c)},X^{(c)}\rangle_s$$

$$+ \sum_{0<s\leq t} [\Phi(X_s)-\Phi(X_{s-})-\Phi'(X_{s-})\Delta X_s].$$

Let us discuss briefly the meaning of the terms appearing in this formula. The first term on the right hand side of the formula is a well defined stochastic integral since locally bounded predictable processes are always integrable and $\Phi'(X_{s-})$ is locally bounded: $|\Phi'(X_{s-})| \leq n$ on $[0,T_n]\setminus(\{0\}\times\Omega)$ where $T_n = \inf\{s: |\Phi'(X_{s-})| > n\}$. The second term is a Stieltjes integral taken pathwise and since $\langle X^c,X^c\rangle$ is continuous, X_{s-} may be replaced with X_s; and the third term is majorized by the convergent series $[\sup_{0\leq s\leq t} |\Phi''(X_s)|]\cdot \sum_s |\Delta X_s|^2 < +\infty$ $\mathbb{P}$-a.e..

An immediate and extremely important consequence of Itô's formula is that $\Phi(X)$ is clearly displayed as a semimartingale. Indeed the stochastic integral is a semimartingale and the second and third terms of the right hand side are processes of finite variation. We mention in passing that from Itô's formula it also follows that

$$[\Phi(X)-\Phi(X_0)]^{(c)} = \Phi'(X_-)\cdot X^{(c)} = \Phi'(X)\cdot X^{(c)}.$$

Two particular cases are noteworthy and in which Itô's formula simplifies. If X is continuous then

$$\Phi(X)-\Phi(X_0) = \Phi'(X)\cdot X + \frac{1}{2}\Phi''(X)\cdot[X,X] \text{ .}$$

If X is of finite variation then

$$\Phi(X_t)-\Phi(X_0) = \int_{]0,t]} \Phi'(X_s)dX_s + \sum_{0<s\leq t} [\Phi(X_s)-\Phi(X_{s-})-\Phi'(X_{s-})\Delta X_s]$$

Returning to the general case $d \geq 1$ with $X = (X^{(1)}, X^{(2)}, \ldots, X^{(d)})$ and $\Phi \in C^2(\mathbb{R}^d,\mathbb{R})$, Itô's Formula takes the form:

$$\Phi(X_t)-\Phi(X_0) = \sum_{k=1}^{d} \int_{]0,t]} \partial_k\Phi(X_{s-})dX_s^{(k)}$$

$$+ \frac{1}{2} \sum_{i,j=1}^{d} \int_{]0,t]} \partial_i\partial_j\Phi(X_s)d\langle (X^{(i)})^{(c)}, (X^{(j)})^{(c)}\rangle$$

$$+ \sum_{0<s\leq t} [\Phi(X_s)-\Phi(X_{s-})-\sum_{k=1}^{d} \partial_k(X_{s-})\Delta X_s^{(k)}] \text{ .}$$

A useful consequence of this formula is the stochastic version of the integration by parts formula. Let X,Y be two real-valued semimartingales and apply Itô's formula to (X,Y) and $\Phi \in C^2(\mathbb{R}^2,\mathbb{R})$ given by $\Phi(x,y) = xy$; the result is:

$$XY-X_0Y_0 = X_-\cdot Y + Y_-\cdot X + \langle X^{(c)},Y^{(c)}\rangle$$

$$+ \sum_{0<s\leq\cdot} \Delta X_s \Delta Y_s$$

or

$$XY = X_-\circ Y + Y_-\circ X + [X,Y] \text{ .}$$

There is also a version of Itô's Formula for C^2-maps between two finite dimensional real vector spaces which is either the previous version applied to each coordinate or, expressed in a much neater fashion the real-valued version but with the substitution of Fréchet derivatives, More precisely, if $\Phi \in C^2(E,F)$ then $\Phi' \in C^1(E,\mathcal{L}(E,F))$ and $\Phi'' \in C(E,\mathcal{L}(E\odot E,F))$ where $E\odot E$ is the symmetric tensor product of E with itself. If M,N are two square integrable E-valued martingales then we can define $<M,N>$ to be the unique predictable $E\odot E$-valued process such that $M\odot N-<M,N>$ is an $E\odot E$-valued martingale which vanishes at time 0 (one can simply delve into a coordinatewise construction). Thus "$\Phi'(X_{s-})dX_s$" $\in F$ and "$\Phi''(X_s)d<X^{(c)},X^{(c)}>_s$" $\in F$ and Itô's formula in this context still takes the form:

$$\Phi(X)-\Phi(X_0) = \Phi'(X_-)\cdot X + \frac{1}{2}\Phi''(X)\cdot<X^{(c)},X^{(c)}>$$

$$+ \sum_{0<s\leq\cdot} [\Phi(X)-\Phi(X_-)-\Phi'(X_-)\Delta X].$$

It will be necessary to have a version of Itô's formula for mappings Φ defined only on an open subset of E in order to discuss portions of the theory of semimartingales with values in a manifold. To this end we proceed in two steps, in both of which $\Phi \in C^2(U,F)$ with U an open subset of E. Consider firstly the special case where X is a semimartingale with values in K, a closed subset of E with $K \subset U$.

Extending Φ from a neighbourhood of K to a C^2 map $\Psi:E \to F$ we can apply Itô's formula to Ψ and X, wherein Ψ can clearly be replaced by Φ.

Before passing to the general case we introduce some notation. For each $\omega \in \Omega$ we denote the closure (at present in E, but in general the ambient space must be specified) of the image of the trajectory $X(\omega)$ by $\overline{X(\omega)}$. Also we denote by X_- the process $t \mapsto X_{t-}$.

Assuming now that $\overline{X(\omega)} \subset U$, or equivalently that X and X_- take their values in U, for almost every $\omega \in \Omega$ (the reason for the latter formulation will become clear in property (3) of page 115), we can define the following stationary sequence of stopping times. Choose an increasing sequence $(U_n)_{n\in\mathbb{N}}$ of relatively compact open sets, whose union is U and such that $\bar{U}_n \subset U$ for every $n \in \mathbb{N}$; define $T_n = \inf\{t: X_t \notin \bar{U}_n\}$. Since X is cadlag, $\overline{X(\omega)}$ is almost surely compact; so $T_n \uparrow\uparrow \overline{+\infty}$. We can apply the previous special case of Itô's formula to Φ and

$$X^{(n)} \equiv \begin{cases} X^{T_n^-} & \text{on } \bar{\mathbb{R}}_+ \times \{T_n > 0\} \\ c \in U \quad \text{(a constant)} & \text{on } \bar{\mathbb{R}}_+ \times \{T_n = 0\} \end{cases} ;$$

$X^{(n)}$ is a bounded semimartingale:

$$X^{(n)} = X^{T_n} - \Delta X_{T_n} 1_{[T_n, +\infty]} 1_{\bar{\mathbb{R}}_+ \times \{T_n > 0\}} - (X_0 - c) 1_{\bar{\mathbb{R}}_+ \times \{T_n = 0\}}.$$

Then on $A_n = \bar{\mathbb{R}}_+ \times \{T_n = +\infty\}$ we can apply the theorems of equivalence of the previous section to $X^{(n)}$ and X in the two integral terms of Itô's formula: $X^{(n)} = X$ and $\Phi'(X^{(n)}_-) = \Phi'(X_-)$ on A_n, so by localization $\Phi'(X^{(n)}_-)\cdot X^{(n)} \sim \Phi'(X_-)\cdot X$ on A_n; $X^{(n)} = X$ on A_n implies that $X^{(n)(c)} \sim X^{(c)}$ on A_n, which in turn implies that $<X^{(n)(c)}, X^{(n)(c)}> \sim <X^{(c)}, X^{(c)}>$ on A_n. Since $A_n(\omega) = \bar{\mathbb{R}}_+$ or ϕ, all the equivalences here are actually equalities, as all terms vanish at time zero. Thus Itô's formula is valid for Φ and X on $\bar{\mathbb{R}}_+ \times \{T_n = +\infty\}$ and therefore on $\bar{\mathbb{R}}_+ \times \Omega$ by stationarity.

We summarize the main result of this section in the

<u>Theorem.</u> Let E,F be finite dimensional real vector spaces, U an open subset of E, X an E-semimartingale with X and X_- taking their values in U, and $\Phi \in C^2(U,F)$. Then <u>(Itô's formula)</u>

$$\Phi(X) - \Phi(X_0) = \Phi'(X_-)\cdot X + \frac{1}{2}\Phi''(X)\cdot <X^{(c)}, X^{(c)}>$$

$$+ \sum_{0<s\leq \cdot} [\Phi(X) - \Phi(X_-) - \Phi'(X_-)\Delta X].$$

In particular the hypothesis is satisfied if U = E or if X takes its values in a closed set $K \subset U$.

CHAPTER 7

SEMIMARTINGALES WITH VALUES IN A MANIFOLD

1. INTRODUCTION

By a *manifold* M we shall always understand a finite dimensional connected C^2-manifold with or without boundary. A *submanifold* N carries the induced topology and may also possess a boundary ∂N provided that either N is open in M or $\partial N \cap \partial M = \phi$. An *embedding* of one manifold M into another N, written $M \hookrightarrow N$, is a C^2 mapping Φ of M into N whose image $\Phi(M)$ is a (not necessarily closed) submanifold of N and which is C^2-diffeomorphic under Φ to M.

There are several possible definitions of a semimartingale with values in a manifold M, or more concisely (and precisely; see further) an M-semimartingale. We begin with a global intrinsic definition delaying a (topologically) local characterization until after a discussion of the localization principle, in the next section. A cadlag adapted map $X:\bar{\mathbb{R}}_+\times\Omega \to M$ is said to be an M-*semimartingale* if $\varphi(X)$ is a real semimartingale for each $\varphi \in C^2(M,\mathbb{R})$. It is easy to see that if the latter condition holds then X is automatically cadlag and adapted. In the case $M = E$, a vector space, this notion of semimartingale coincides with our original definition. Indeed if X is an E-semimartingale in the sense that $\varphi(X)$ is a real semimartingale for all $\varphi \in C^2(E,\mathbb{R})$, then in particular we can choose the coordinate functions with respect to any basis of E, and recover the original definition. Conversely, Itô's Formula supplies the implication in the opposite direction.

It follows immediately from the definition that if $\Phi:M \to N$ is C^2 and X is an M-semimartingale then $\Phi(X)$ is an N-semimartingale.

Another important property, of a hereditary nature, is that if $N \hookrightarrow M$ and X is an M-semimartingale with values in N satisfying $X(\omega)$, $X_-(\omega) \subset N$ a.e., then X is an N-semimartingale. To see this we first indicate a special case, namely where M = E a vector space, and N is a submanifold of E. Here we choose an open set U of E containing N such that N is closed in U. Then given a $\varphi \in C^2(N,\mathbb{R})$ we extend it to a $\bar{\varphi} \in C^2(U,\mathbb{R})$ (it is well known that such an extension exists by a localization and partition of unity argument), and apply Itô's formula to $\bar{\varphi}(X) = \varphi(X)$ to conclude that $\varphi(X)$

is a semimartingale and hence that X is an N-semimartingale. To pass the general case we appeal to a theorem of Whitney which asserts that M can be embedded into $\mathbb{R}^{2d}$ (as a closed submanifold, moreover) where d = dimension of M. Then $N \subset M \subset \mathbb{R}^{2d}$ and X is an M-semimartingale, therefore an E-semimartingale. Since X and X_- are N-valued, we conclude from the special case that X is an N-semimartingale.

Finally, to indicate the utility of a theory of M-valued semimartingales even in the context of studying processes taking values in a linear space, consider the following example. Suppose we wish to study the angle (as in polar coordinates) of a 2-dimensional Brownian motion B issuing from a point other than the origin (to which it almost surely never visits), or perhaps logB, considering $\mathbb{R}^2$ as the complex plane. Due to the nature of B, each of these is a bona fide multivalued function $\varphi(B)$ so that we are immediately faced with the problem of lifting B to a semimartingale $\tilde{B}$ with values in a (universal) covering space M, $M \overset{\pi}{\to} \mathbb{R}^2\setminus\{0\}$, on which φ becomes a single valued C^2 function $\tilde{\varphi}$; $\tilde{\varphi}\circ\tilde{B}$ would then be a single valued semimartingale which could be studied in place of $\varphi(B)$. It turns out that such a $\tilde{B}$ can be constructed but before casting this property into a general form we review some of the topological terminology involved.

Recall that a manifold $\tilde{M}$ is a covering of M with covering map π if $\pi:\tilde{M} \to M$ is a C^2 surjection with the property that each point $m \in M$ has a neighbourhood U such that $\pi^{-1}(U)$ is a disjoint union $\bigcup_{n \in \mathbb{N}} V_n$, V_n open, with $\pi|_{V_n} : V_n \to U$ a diffeomorphism. Each continuous curve $\gamma : \bar{\mathbb{R}}_+ \to M$ has a lifting $\tilde{\gamma}$ $(\pi\tilde{\gamma} = \gamma)$ which is unique if $\tilde{\gamma}(0)$ is prescribed, this is a classical theorem of topology.

The lifting property we are seeking is as follows. Given a continuous M-semimartingale X and a covering $\pi:\tilde{M} \to M$ then there exists a continuous $\tilde{M}$-semimartingale $\tilde{X}$ which is a lifting of X $(\pi\tilde{X} = X)$ and which is unique if $\tilde{X}_0 \in \mathcal{T}_0$ is prescribed. In other words (rather a picture) we have the following commutative diagram:

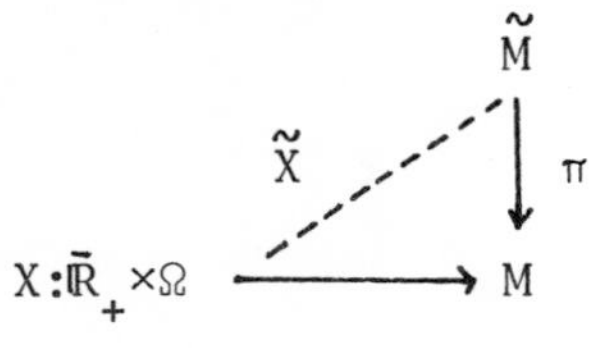

We delay the proof of this property until after a discussion of the localization principle, but remark at this point that the lifting is obtained in a purely deterministic manner, trajectory by trajectory, and whose existence is guaranteed by the topological theorem admitted above. The issue at hand is whether or not $\tilde{X}$ is an $\tilde{M}$-semimartingale.

2. LOCALIZATION PRINCIPLE; APPLICATIONS

Localization Principle. If $(A_n)_{n\in\mathbb{N}}$ is a sequence of optional open sets which cover an optional compact set $A \subset \bar{\mathbb{R}}_+\times\Omega$, and X is a function defined on A with values in a manifold M such that on each $A\cap A_n$, X is the restriction of an M-semimartingale, then X is the restriction of an M-semimartingale to A as well. In particular for $A = \bar{\mathbb{R}}_+\times\Omega$, X is a semimartingale. □

We shall give the proof of the localization principle in the case $A=\bar{\mathbb{R}}_+\times\Omega$ preceeded by a succession of four lemmas. That the principle is false, if the compactness assumption is dropped, can be seen from the following deterministic example (recall that a deterministic semimartingale is just a cadlag function of bounded variation). Let $X = 0$ on $A_1 = \bigcup_{n\in\mathbb{N}}]2n,2n+1[$ and $X = 1$ on $A_2 = \bigcup_{n\in\mathbb{N}}]2n+1,2n+2[$; A_1 and A_2 are open. On A_1, X is the restriction of the constant function 0; on A_2, X is the restriction of the constant function 1. However on $A = A_1\cup A_2$, X has a unique cadlag extension which is not of bounded variation.

Lemma 1. Let X be a real-valued process and $T_n \uparrow\uparrow \overline{+\infty}$ or $+\infty$ such that each X^{T_n} is a semimartingale. Then X is a semimartingale.

Proof. Let $\varphi \in$ BPre, then $(\varphi\cdot X^{T_n})^{T_{n-1}} = \varphi\cdot(X^{T_n})^{T_{n-1}} = \varphi\cdot X^{T_{n-1}}$ i.e. $\varphi\cdot X^{T_n} = \varphi\cdot X^{T_{n-1}}$ on $[0,T_{n-1}]$.

Thus for almost every $\omega \in \Omega$ and large n (both independent of φ) $\mu_{X^{T_n}}(\varphi) = (\varphi \cdot X^{T_n})_{+\infty}$ is eventually constant in $n \in \mathbb{N}$. We define this common value to be the random variable $\mu(\varphi) := \lim_{n\to+\infty} \mu_{X^{T_n}}(\varphi)$ a.s.. Clearly $\mu(1_{]0,t]}) = X_t$ is adapted and localizable so by Dellacherie's theorem it suffices to show that μ is a measure adapted and localizable; the last part is evident. To this end let $\varepsilon > 0$ and $(\varphi_m)_{m\in N} \subset$ BPre be given where $\varphi_m \to 0$ pointwise and $|\varphi_m| \leq 1$. Then

$$\mathbb{P}\{|\mu(\varphi_m)|>\varepsilon\} \leq \mathbb{P}\{|\mu(\varphi_m)-\mu_{X^{T_n}}(\varphi_m)| \geq \frac{\varepsilon}{2}\} + \mathbb{P}\{|\mu_{X^{T_n}}(\varphi_m)| > \frac{\varepsilon}{2}\}$$

$$\leq \mathbb{P}\{T_n<+\infty \text{ or } \overline{+\infty}\} + \mathbb{P}\{|\mu_{X^{T_n}}(\varphi_m)| \geq \frac{\varepsilon}{2}\} .$$

Choose n sufficiently large that the first term is less than $\varepsilon/2$. For this n choose m_0 such that $m \geq m_0$ implies that the second term is also less than $\varepsilon/2$. □

<u>Lemma 2.</u> Suppose a real-valued process X coincides on $[0,T_n[$, where $T_n \uparrow\uparrow \overline{+\infty}$, with a semimartingale $X_{(n)}$, $n \in \mathbb{N}$. Then X is a semimartingale.

<u>Proof.</u> Since X is optional $X_{T_n} \in \mathcal{T}_{T_n}$ and $X^{T_n} = X_{(n)}^{T_n} + [(\Delta X)_{T_n} - (\Delta X_{(n)})_{T_n}] \cdot 1_{[T_n,+\infty]}$ is a semimartingale. Lemma (1) applies and we are done. □

Remark. Lemmas (1) and (2) are easily extended to semimartingales with values in a manifold.

A subset $A \subset \bar{\mathbb{R}}_+ \times \Omega$ is said to be a *semimartingale set* if 1_A is a semimartingale. In particular 1_A is cadlag which implies the existence of a stationary sequence $S_0 \leq T_0 \leq S_1 \leq T_1 \leq \ldots$ such that $A = \bigcup_n [S_n, T_n[$. It is known that a convex function of a real semimartingale is again a semimartingale. Since the minimum of two numbers a,b can be expressed as $a \wedge b = \frac{1}{2}(a+b-|a-b|)$ and $a \mapsto |a|$ is convex, we see that the minimum, and hence the maximum, of two semimartingales is again a semimartingale. Thus the class of semimartingale sets is stable under finite intersections and unions as well as complimentation.

Lemma 3. Let X be an M-valued process and $(A_j)_{j=1}^n$ semimartingale sets. If on each A_j, X coincides with the restriction of a semimartingale $X^{(j)}$, $1 \leq j \leq n$, then X coincides with the restriction of a semimartingale on $A = \bigcup_{j=1}^n A_j$ as well.

Proof. Without loss of generality we can assume that the A_j, $1 \leq j \leq n$, are disjoint. Embed M into a Euclidean space E as a closed submanifold and define $\tilde{X} := \sum_{j=1}^n 1_{A_j} X^{(j)} + m 1_{A^c}$ where m is a fixed point of M. Then $\tilde{X}$ is an E-semimartingale with values in M; hence an

M-semimartingale which clearly coincides with X on A. □

A subset $A \subset \bar{\mathbb{R}}_+ \times \Omega$ is said to be a *stationary union* of a sequence of subsets $(A_n)_{n\in\mathbb{N}}$, written $A = \biguplus_{n\in\mathbb{N}} A_n$, if each section $A(\omega)$ is a finite union thereof.

Lemma 4. Let X be an M-valued process and $A = \biguplus_{n\in\mathbb{N}} A_n$ with each A_n a semimartingale set. If $X|_{A_n} = X^{(n)}|_{A_n}$ where each $X^{(n)}$ is a semimartingale then X coincides on A with the restriction of a semimartingale as well.

Proof. By Lemma (3) we can assume without loss of generality that $A_n \uparrow\uparrow A$ i.e. $A_n \uparrow A$ and $A(\omega) = A_n(\omega)$ for some n depending on ω. Define $T_n(\omega) = \inf\{t : 1_{A_n(\omega)}(t) \neq 1_{A(\omega)}(t)\}$, so that $A_n \cap [0,T_n[\;= A \cap [0,T_n[$ (possibly both empty) for each $n \in \mathbb{N}$. Then $A_n \uparrow\uparrow A$ implies that $T_n \uparrow\uparrow \overline{+\infty}$.

Let $\tilde{X} = X^{(j)}$ on $[T_{j-1},T_j[$, $j \in \mathbb{N}$, and $\tilde{X}^{(n)} = \tilde{X}$ on $[0,T_n[$, and a constant $m \in M$ on $[T_n,+\infty]$. By Lemma (3) $\tilde{X}^{(n)}$ is a semimartingale and so Lemma (2) implies that $\tilde{X}$ is a semimartingale. Now,

$$\tilde{X}|_{[T_n,T_{n+1}[\cap A} = X^{(n+1)}|_{[T_n,T_{n+1}[\cap A} = X^{(n+1)}|_{[T_n,T_{n+1}[\cap A_{n+1}}$$

$$= X|_{[T_n,T_{n+1}[\cap A_{n+1}} = X|_{[T_n,T_{n+1}[\cap A} .$$

Since $\bigcup_n [T_n,T_{n+1}[\;= \bar{\mathbb{R}}_+ \times \Omega$, $\tilde{X}|_A = X|_A$. □

Proof of the localization principle in the case $A = \bar{\mathbb{R}}_+ \times \Omega$: Define for each $s \in \bar{\mathbb{R}}_+$ and $n \in \mathbb{N}$ $S_{n,s}(\omega) := \inf\{t \geq s: t \notin A_n(\omega)\}$. Since A_n is open and optional, $S_{n,s}$ is a stopping time and $A_n = \bigcup_{s \in \mathbb{Q}_+} [s, S_{n,s}[^\circ$. Therefore

$\bar{\mathbb{R}}_+ \times \Omega = \bigcup_{s \in \mathbb{Q}_+, n \in \mathbb{N}} [s, S_{n,s}[^\circ$, the stationarity of the union following from the compactness of A. Clearly we also have $\bar{\mathbb{R}}_+ \times \Omega = \bigcup_{s \in \mathbb{Q}_+, n \in \mathbb{N}} [s, S_{n,s}[$ where each $[s, S_{n,s}[$ is a semimartingale set. By right continuity we have that X agrees with an M-semimartingale not only on $[s, S_{n,s}[^\circ$ but all of $[s, S_{n,s}[$. Lemma (4) applies and the theorem is proved. □

Applications. The localization principle enables us to make the following generalization of a semimartingale due to Meyer and Stricker. Given an open subset A of $\bar{\mathbb{R}}_+ \times \Omega$, a process $X: A \to M$ is called *a locally defined M-semimartingale* if X is the restriction of an optional process to A (briefly, X is optional) and if there exists an open covering $(A_n)_{n \in \mathbb{N}}$ of A and (globally defined) semimartingales $(X_{(n)})_{n \in \mathbb{N}}$ such that $X|_{A \cap A_n} = X_{(n)}|_{A \cap A_n}$. In the case $A = \bar{\mathbb{R}}_+ \times \Omega$ the localization principle says that this new notion of a semimartingale coincides with the original one, so that we have consistency in nomenclature. If Y is an optional extension of X to $\bar{\mathbb{R}}_+ \times \Omega$ then we can arrange to have an optional open covering by replacing A_n with $\{Y = X_{(n)}\}^{\circ}$, $n \in \mathbb{N}$.

As an example consider $1/B$ on $A = \{B \neq 0\}$ where B is a one-dimensional Brownian motion. Here we can take the covering $\{B \neq 0\} \subset \bigcup_{\substack{s \in \mathbb{Q}_+ \\ n \in \mathbb{N}}} [s, S_{n,s}[^{\circ}$, where $S_{n,s} = \inf\{t \geq s : |B_t| \leq 1/n\}$, and semimartingale extensions:

$$X_{(n,s)} = \begin{cases} \text{a constant on } [0,s[\times\Omega \cup [s,+\infty]\times\{S_{n,s}=s\} \\ 1/B^{S_{n,s}} \quad \text{on } [s,+\infty]\times\{S_{n,s}>s\} \end{cases} ;$$

$X_{(n,s)}$ is a semimartingale by the localization principle or rather Lemma (3). Another argument will be given shortly.

In the case $A = \mathbb{R}_+ \times \Omega$ there is a simple equivalent definition of a semimartingale defined on A. Namely, $X : \mathbb{R}_+ \times \Omega \to M$ is a semimartingale if for all stopping times T, with $T < +\infty$, $X|_{[0,T]}$ is a semimartingale i.e. X^T is a semimartingale; or what is equivalent: X coincides on $[0,T]$ with a (globally defined) semimartingale $\bar{X}$. Indeed if the situation above holds then we can take $A_n = [0,n[$ in the original definition since $A_n \cap A = A_n$, $X|_{[0,n[} = X^n|_{[0,n[}$ and X^n is a semimartingale. (We observe that the hypothesis can be weakened to read: there exists a sequence $(T_n)_{n \in \mathbb{N}}$ of stopping times with $T_n < +\infty$ and $T_n \uparrow +\infty$, such that X^{T_n} is a semimartingale.) In the opposite direction, if $X : \mathbb{R}_+ \times \Omega \to M$ is a semimartingale, according to our original definition, then there exist optional open sets A_n covering $\mathbb{R}_+\times\Omega$, and (globally defined) semimartingales $X_{(n)}$ such that $X|_{A\cap A_n} = X_{(n)}|_{A\cap A_n}$. Therefore $X|_{[0,T]\cap A_n} = X_{(n)}|_{[0,T]\cap A_n}$. By the localization principle X coincides on [0,T] with a (global defined) semimartingale $\bar{X}$, since [0,T] is compact and optional.

We now list five properties of locally defined semimartingales, some of which are extensions of properties of globally defined semimartingales.

(1) If a process X is optional on $A = \bigcup_{n\in\mathbb{N}} A_n$ where each A_n is open and $X|_{A_n}$ is a semimartingale, then X is a semimartingale; this is immediate from the definition.

(2) If $\Phi \in C^2(M,N)$ and X is a locally defined M-semimartingale then $\Phi(X)$ is a locally defined N-semimartingale; this is also immediate from the definition.

(3) If $X:A \to M \hookrightarrow N$ is an N-semimartingale with values in M and $X(\omega)$, $X_-(\omega) \subset M$ a.e., then X is an M-semimartingale. (Note that "$X(\omega), X_-(\omega) \subset M$" is weaker than "$\overline{X(\omega)} \subset M$.")

The proof of this property is a good illustration of the localization principle, and so we give it. By the Whitney embedding theorem and property (2) we can reduce to the case $X:A \to M \subset E$, a Euclidean space. As in the definition we have an open covering $A \subset \bigcup_{n\in\mathbb{N}} A_n$ and globally defined semimartingales $X_{(n)}$ such that $X|_{A\cap A_n} = X_{(n)}|_{A\cap A_n}$. Choose an increasing sequence $(K_m)_{m\in\mathbb{N}}$ of compact subsets of M such that $K_n \subset \mathring{K}_{n+1}$, $M = \bigcup_m K_m$ and define for each $(n,m,s) \in \mathbb{N}^2\times\mathbb{Q}_+$ the stopping time $S_{(n,m,s)}(\omega) = \inf\{t\geq s : X_{(n)}(t,\omega) \notin K_m\}$. Set

$$X_{(n,m,s)} = \begin{cases} \text{a constant} \in K_n, & \text{on } [0,s[\times\Omega \cup [s,+\infty]\times\{S_{(n,m,s)}=s\} \\ X_{(n)}^{S^-_{(n,m,s)}} & \text{on } [s,+\infty]\times\{S_{(n,m,s)} > s\} \end{cases}$$

By Lemma (3) of the localization principle, $X_{(n,m,s)}$ is an E-semimartingale, with values in $K_m \subset M$ so that $\overline{X_{(n,m,s)}(\omega)} \subset K_m \subset M$. Thus $X_{(n,m,s)}$ is an M-semimartingale, On $A \cap (A_n\cap[s,S_{(n,m,s)}[^\circ)$, $X = X_{(n)} = X_{(n,m,s)}$, so it remains to show that $A \subset \bigcup_{\substack{s\in\mathbb{Q}_+\\ n\in\mathbb{N}}} (A_n \cap [s,S_{(n,m,s)}[^\circ)$. For instance, if $(t,\omega) \in A\cap A_n$ and $t\neq 0, +\infty$: choose $m \in \mathbb{N}$ such that $\mathring{K}_m \supset \{p_1,p_2\}$ where $p_1 = X_{(n)}(t^-,\omega) \in M$ and $p_2 = X_{(n)}(t,\omega) \in M$. Since $X_{(n)}$ is cadlag we can choose $0 < s \in \mathbb{Q}_+$ and $t' > t$ such that $X_{(n)}(r,\omega) \in K_m$ for $r \in [s,t']$. Then $S_{(n,m,s)}(\omega) \geq t'$, or $(t,\omega) \in]s,S_{(n,m,s)}[$. The cases $t=0,+\infty$ are also easily handled. □

A good illustration of these properties comes in an alternate proof of a generalization of the previous example. Let X be an $\mathbb{R}$-valued continuous semimartingale, so that $A = X^{-1}(\mathbb{R}\setminus\{0\})$ is open. Denoting by $\tilde{\mathbb{R}}$ the one-point compactification of $\mathbb{R}$, X is also an $\tilde{\mathbb{R}}$-semimartingale. Since $x \mapsto 1/x$ is a diffeomorphism of $\tilde{\mathbb{R}}$, $1/X$ is also an $\tilde{\mathbb{R}}$-semimartingale (over $\bar{\mathbb{R}}_+ \times \Omega$ still). On A it takes its values in $\mathbb{R}$, and of course $X_- = X$, therefore $1/X$ is an $\mathbb{R}$-semimartingale over A.

(4) A process $X: A \to M$ is a semimartingale iff $\varphi(X)$ is a real semimartingale for all $\varphi \in C^2(M) = C^2(M,\mathbb{R})$.

The "only if" part of this property is a special case of property (2). The converse is not deduced from the global version, which was actually the definition, but rather is a consequence of properties (2) and (3). To see this, observe that it suffices, by the Whitney embedding theorem, to consider the case $M \subset R^d$, i.e. M being a closed submanifold of a Euclidean space, say of dimension d = 2 dim M. Let $(e_i)_{1 \leq i \leq 2d}$ be the canonical basis of $\mathbb{R}^d$ and $X^{(i)}$ the i-th coordinate of X with respect to this basis. The coordinate functions being C^2, each $X^{(i)}$ is real semimartingale. It is almost immediate from the definition that a d-tuple of (locally defined) semimartingales is a semimartingale in the product. Thus X is an E-semimartingale. As M is closed, X and X_- take their values in M, hence X is an M-semimartingale. □

Frequently one is led to perform various calculations in a coordinate chart of M. It is therefore convenient to have a topologically local description of a continuous M-semimartingale. If $(\mathcal{V},\Phi)$ is a chart on M and $X:A \to M$ a continuous semimartingale then $X^{-1}(\mathcal{V})$ is open and $X_{\mathcal{V}} := X|_{X^{-1}(\mathcal{V})}$ is a $\mathcal{V}$-semimartingale. Indeed, it is an M-semimartingale with values in $\mathcal{V}$ and $X_- = X$ by continuity; therefore by property (3) above it is a $\mathcal{V}$-semimartingale. Conversely if A is open and $X:A \to M$ a continuous process such that $X_{(n)} := X|_{X^{-1}(\mathcal{V}_n)}$ is a $\mathcal{V}_n$-semimartingale for each $\mathcal{V}_n$ from a family $(\mathcal{V}_n,\Phi_n)_{n\in\mathbb{N}}$ of charts covering M, then X is an M-semimartingale. Indeed by property (2), X is an M-semimartingale on $X^{-1}(\mathcal{V}_n)$ and $A = \bigcup_n X^{-1}(\mathcal{V}_n)$. Note that $X_{(n)}$ is a $\mathcal{V}_n$-semimartingale iff $\Phi_n(X_{(n)})$ is an E-semimartingale where $\Phi_n:\mathcal{V}_n \to E$. To summarize:

(5) If $A \subset \bar{\mathbb{R}}_+\times\Omega$ is open, $X:A \to M$ is a continuous process, and $(\mathcal{V}_n,\Phi_n)_{n\in\mathbb{N}}$ is a family of charts covering M with $\Phi_n:\mathcal{V}_n \to E$, then X is an M-semimartingale iff $\Phi_n(X|_{X^{-1}(\mathcal{V}_n)})$ is an E-semimartingale for each $n \in \mathbb{N}$.

We are now in a position to sketch a proof of the lifting property of semimartingales, stated in the introduction to this chapter. Recall that we are given a continuous semimartingale $X:\bar{\mathbb{R}}_+\times\Omega \to M$, a covering $\pi:\tilde{M} \to M$, and $\tilde{X}_0 \in \mathcal{T}_0$, and we wish to show that the (pathwise) lifting $\tilde{X}$ of X is also a semimartingale. The proof that $\tilde{X}$ is adapted is measure theoretic and independent of the notions presently being discussed; and so it will be omitted. Now, choose a covering of M consisting of charts $(\mathcal{V}_n,\Phi_n)_{n\in\mathbb{N}}$ such that $\pi^{-1}\mathcal{V}_n = \bigcup_{k\in\mathbb{N}} \tilde{\mathcal{V}}_{n,k}$ (disjoint) with $\tilde{\mathcal{V}}_{n,k} \cong \mathcal{V}_n$ under $\pi_{n,k} := \pi|_{\tilde{\mathcal{V}}_{n,k}}$. Then $(\tilde{\mathcal{V}}_{n,k}, \Phi_n\circ\pi_{n,k})_{(n,k)\in\mathbb{N}^2}$ is a family of charts covering $\tilde{M}$ and $\tilde{X}^{-1}(\tilde{\mathcal{V}}_{n,k}) = X^{-1}(\pi^{-1}_{n,k}\mathcal{V}_n) = X^{-1}(\mathcal{V}_n)$. Since $X|_{X^{-1}(\mathcal{V}_n)}$ is a $\mathcal{V}_n$-semimartingale then $\tilde{X}|_{\tilde{X}^{-1}(\mathcal{V}_{n,k})} = \pi^{-1}_{n,k}(X|_{X^{-1}(\mathcal{V}_n)})$ is a $(\pi^{-1}_{n,k}\mathcal{V}_n) = \mathcal{V}_{n,k}$-semimartingale, and by the discussion leading up to property (5) we are done.

3. APPENDIX: INTEGRATION WITH RESPECT TO A LOCALLY DEFINED SEMIMARTINGALE

In this appendix we give a brief sketch of how stochastic integration may be extended to continuous vector-valued locally defined semimartingales.

If $A \subset \bar{\mathbb{R}}_+ \times \Omega$ is open, E is a finite dimensional real vector space, and $X : A \to E$ is a continuous semimartingale, then it can be shown that there exists a continuous <u>formal</u> semimartingale $\tilde{X}$ such that $X \underset{A}{\sim} \tilde{X}$. Here the equivalence means that there exists an open covering $(A_n)_{n \in \mathbb{N}}$ and globally defined semimartingales $(X_{(n)})_{n \in \mathbb{N}}$ such that on $A \cap A_n$: $X \sim X_{(n)}$ with $X_{(n)} \sim \tilde{X}$.

Given any continuous formal semimartingale Y and an optional process H on A, say with an optional extension $\bar{H}$ to $\bar{\mathbb{R}}_+ \times \Omega$, we define $H \cdot Y$ to be the class of continuous formal semimartingales equivalent on A to the formal semimartingale $\bar{H} \cdot Y$. The resulting class does not depend on the choice of the extension $\bar{H}$ and would coincide with $\bar{H} \cdot \tilde{Y}$ if $Y \underset{A}{\sim} \tilde{Y} \in \mathrm{Opt}\mathcal{SM}^c$. As such we define $H \cdot X$ to be the continuous equivalence class on A of $\bar{H} \cdot \tilde{X}$; the resulting class depends neither on the choice of optional extension $\bar{H}$ of H nor the continuous formal semimartingale $\tilde{X}$, equivalent to X on A.

To see that this definition is fruitful we note that it coincides with the previous definition when $A = \bar{\mathbb{R}}_+ \times \Omega$, that it is bilinear in H and X (for fixed A), and that if K is another optional process on A then $K \cdot (H \cdot X) = (KH) \circ X$ (equality of equivalence classes). We also write dX for the continuous equivalence class of X and HdX for $H \circ X$; thus $K(HdX) = (KH)dX$. Most important is the analogue of Itô's formula. Let $X:A \to U$ where U is open in E and $\Phi \in C^2(U,F)$, where F is another finite dimensional real vector space. Then

$$d\Phi(X) = \Phi'(X)dX + \frac{1}{2}\Phi''(X)d[X,X] .$$

Let us make precise the meaning of each of the terms above. On the left hand side, $d\Phi(X)$ stands for the class of continuous formal semimartingales equivalent on A to $\Phi(X)$; any one of them depicted by $\widetilde{\Phi(X)}$. On the right hand side: $\Phi'(X)dX$ is the class of continuous formal semimartingales equivalent on A to $\Phi'(\bar{X})\cdot\tilde{X}$, where $\bar{X}$ is any optional extension of X on A to $\mathbb{R}_+\times\Omega$ and $\tilde{X} \in \mathrm{Opt}\mathcal{SM}_0^c$ with $X \underset{A}{\sim} \tilde{X}$ (note: it is pointless to write $\Phi'(X_-)dX$ since we must extend X_- optionally and we have the optional stochastic integral at our disposal). Similarly $\frac{1}{2}\Phi''(X)d[X,X]$ is the continuous equivalence class of $\frac{1}{2}\Phi''(\bar{X})\cdot[\tilde{X},\tilde{X}]$. Therefore we could also write: $\widetilde{\Phi(X)} \underset{A}{\sim} \Phi'(\bar{X})\circ\tilde{X} + \frac{1}{2}\Phi''(\bar{X})\cdot[\tilde{X},\tilde{X}]$, which is what one would establish to verify Itô's formula, and which conveys the real importance - telling us how to integrate with respect to $\Phi(X)$ in terms of X.

As a simple example, if B is a one dimensional Brownian motion then on $A = \{B\neq 0\} \subset \mathbb{R}_+\times\Omega$

$$d(1/B) = (-1/B^2)dB + (1/B^3)dt .$$

Note that in this case $\{B=0\}$ is both dB- and dt-negligible so that we can already form the formal semimartingale $(-1/B^2)\cdot B+(1/B^3)\cdot(t)$ on some $\Re_\tau = [0,\tau]\times\Omega$, and there it is equivalent to $\{B\neq 0\}\cap\Re_\tau$ to $1/B$ (we have replaced $\bar{\mathbb{R}}_+$ with $[0,\tau]$ in order that μ_B would exist).

CHAPTER 8

STOCHASTIC INTEGRATION ON A MANIFOLD

1. ORIENTATION

In this section we shall try to establish a connection, on an informal level, between stochastic differentials and second order differential geometry.

Let X be a continuous semimartingale with values in E, a finite dimensional real vector space and $x:\mathbb{R} \to E$ a C^2 curve. Also let $\Phi:E \to F$, F being a second finite dimensional real vector space, and let us compare $Y = \Phi(X)$ and $y = \Phi(x)$ on an infinitesimal level. At each instant t, $\dot{x}(t)$ and $\dot{y}(t)$ are vectors in E and F respectively which are tangent to the curves x and y at the points x(t) and y(t) respectively. They are related by the following equation

$$\dot{y}(t) = \Phi'(x(t))\dot{x}(t).$$

Recalling Itô's formula in differential form

$$dY_t = \Phi'(X_t)dX_t + \frac{1}{2}\Phi''(X_t)d[X,X]_t$$

(since X is continuous $[X,X] = \langle X^{(c)}, X^{(c)}\rangle$, the unique predictable cadlag $E \odot E$ - valued process such that $X^{(c)} \odot X^{(c)} - \langle X^{(c)}, X^{(c)}\rangle$ is a local martingale vanishing at time zero. We will stay with the former notation, it being simpler and less apt to be confused with a pairing, of which we shall see a few in the next section), we see that dX_t does not transform as a first order infinitesimal. Since the infinitesimal $\frac{1}{2}d[X,X]_t$ figures into the transformation it is natural to keep track of the pair $(dX_t, \frac{1}{2}d[X,X]_t)$ and see it if transforms in some recognizable geometrical fashion i.e. does $(dY_t, \frac{1}{2}d[Y,Y]_t)$ depend on $(dX_t, \frac{1}{2}d[X,X]_t)$ through a linear transformation? Indeed it does; from Itô's formula we see that

$$\frac{1}{2}d[Y,Y]_t \;=\; \Phi'(X_t) \circledcirc \Phi'(X_t)\frac{1}{2}d[X,X]_t$$

since $[\Phi'(X)\cdot X, \Phi'(X)\cdot X] = \Phi'(X) \circledcirc \Phi'(X)\cdot[X,X]$ where the dot is of course stochastic integration and where $\circledcirc$ denotes the symmetric tensor product map of two linear maps i.e. if $\mathcal{L}_1, \mathcal{L}_2 : E \to F$ are linear then $\mathcal{L}_1 \circledcirc \mathcal{L}_2 : E \odot E \to F \odot F$ is the linear map induced by the symmetric bilinear map of $E\times E \to F\odot F$ given by $(e_1, e_2) \mapsto \frac{1}{2}(\mathcal{L}_1 e_1 \odot \mathcal{L}_2 e_2 + \mathcal{L}_1 e_2 \odot \mathcal{L}_2 e_1)$. Thus denoting what we shall call the *complete semimartingale* by :

$$\underline{X} := \begin{pmatrix} X \\ \frac{1}{2}[X,X] \end{pmatrix} \text{ and its informal differential by } d\underline{X}_t = \begin{pmatrix} dX_t \\ \frac{1}{2}d[X,X]_t \end{pmatrix}$$

we can write in a compact notation

$$d\underline{Y}_t = \begin{pmatrix} \Phi'(X_t) & \Phi''(X_t) \\ 0 & \Phi'(X_t) \circledcirc \Phi'(X_t) \end{pmatrix} d\underline{X}_t$$

in the usual sense of matrix multiplication.

To find the geometrical significance of this transformation law it is natural to look at the accelerations of x and y - how else could we bring in the second derivative of Φ? Well,

$$\dot{y}(t) = \Phi'(x(t))\dot{x}(t)$$

$$\ddot{y}(t) = \Phi'(x(t)) + \Phi''(x(t))\dot{x}(t) \odot \dot{x}(t)$$

so that the *complete acceleration* $\underline{\ddot{x}} := \begin{pmatrix} \ddot{x} \\ \dot{x} \odot \dot{x} \end{pmatrix}$ transforms in the same fashion:

$$\underline{\ddot{y}}(t) = \begin{pmatrix} \Phi'(x(t)) & \Phi''(x(t)) \\ 0 & \Phi'(x(t)) \circledcirc \Phi'(x(t)) \end{pmatrix} \underline{\ddot{x}}(t) .$$

The complete acceleration of a curve is a second order tangent vector in the sense of second order differential geometry of which we give an introduction in the next section. Lest the reader have the wool pulled over his eyes, $\underline{\ddot{x}}(t)$ exists for all t in a mathematically rigorous way, whereas $d\underline{X}_t$, as dX_t, exists only globally as a measure (think of $\mu(dx)$ and $f\mu(dx)$) so that the theory of second order differential geometry cannot simply be applied. Rather global analogues of the second order operations and apparatus will be found in the guise of indefinite integration. These will be constructed in the third section. At any rate, it is pleasant and fruitful to think of $\underline{dX}_t$ heuristically as a second order tangent vector at the point X_t.

2. SECOND ORDER DIFFERENTIAL GEOMETRY: $T^1(M)$ AND $T^2(M)$

Suppose that M is a C^1 manifold. We endow $C^1(M,\mathbb{R})$ with the complete metrizable topology of uniform convergence of functions and their first derivatives on compact sets (the reader is invited to make this precise with charts) and for each $x \in M$ define the tangent space of M at x, written $T^1(M,x)$, to be the subset of $C^1(M,\mathbb{R})^*$ (the dual of C^1) consisting of elements ξ_x which have their supports $\subset \{x\}$ (i.e. if $\varphi \in C^1$ and $\text{supp}\varphi \cap \{x\} = \phi$ then $(\varphi|\xi_x) \equiv (\varphi,\xi_x)_1 := \xi_x(\varphi) = 0$) and such that $(1|\xi_x) = 0$.

As a generic example, if $(\mathcal{V},\Phi)$ is a chart about $x \in M$ then the partial derivatives $\partial_i \in T^1(M,x)$ for $1 \le i \le \dim M$ where $\partial_i\varphi := \frac{\partial}{\partial x_i}(\varphi|_{\mathcal{V}}\circ\Phi^{-1})|_{\Phi(x)}$, the derivative taken in the usual sense. It can be shown that if $\xi_x \in T^1(M,x)$ then $\xi_x = \Sigma b^k\partial_k$ where necessarily $b^k = (\alpha\Phi_k|\xi_x)$, for $\alpha \in C^1(M)$ with $\text{supp}\alpha \subset \mathcal{V}$ and $\alpha = 1$ on a neighbourhood of x (as such $\alpha\Phi_k$ can be extended off $\mathcal{V}$ to all of M with value 0 on $M\backslash\mathcal{V}$) where Φ_k is the k-th Euclidean coordinate of Φ. In particular $\dim T^1(M,x) = \dim M$. Thus we have replaced the illusory arrow, which has nowhere to live, with differentiation in the direction in which the arrow is pointing. More precisely if $\gamma:\mathbb{R} \to M$ is C^1 with $\gamma(0) = x$, then we can define an element $\dot{\gamma} \in T^1(M,x)$ by $(\varphi|\dot{\gamma}) = \frac{d}{dt}(\varphi\circ\gamma)|_{t=0}$. It is not hard to show that every element of $T^1(M,x)$ can be expressed in this manner. In particular $\partial_i = \dot{\gamma}$ where $\gamma = \Phi\circ\gamma_i$ and where $\gamma_i(t) = te_i$, e_i being the i-th canonical basis element of $\mathbb{R}^d$, $d = \dim M$.

In the case where M is an open subset of E, a finite dimensional real vector space we will use this representation to make the identification $T^1(M,x) = E$ through the correspondence $v \mapsto \partial_v$ where $(\varphi|\partial_v) := \lim_{t\to 0} (\varphi(x+tv)-\varphi(x))/t$, the directional derivative of φ at x in the direction v. If $(e_i)_{i=1}^d$ is a basis of E then in this identification $e_i \mapsto \partial_i$ so that $\Sigma b^k\partial_k \leftrightarrow \Sigma b^k e_k$.

Returning to the general setting, recall that a first order differential operator without term of order zero is a continuous linear map $\xi:C^1(M,\mathbb{R}) \to C^0(M,\mathbb{R})$ which is local (in the sense that if $\varphi \in C^1(M,\mathbb{R})$ is zero in an open subset of M then so also is $\xi\varphi$) and such that $\xi 1 = 0$. If ξ is such an operator then for each $x \in M$, $\xi_x \in T^1(M,x)$ where

$(\varphi|\xi_x) := (\xi\varphi)(x)$. Conversely, if we have an assignment $x \mapsto \xi_x \in T^1(M,x)$ for each $x \in M$, such that for all $\varphi \in C^1(M,\mathbb{R})$ $x \mapsto (\varphi|\xi_x)$ is continuous then we have a first order differential operator without constant term ξ given by $(\xi\varphi)(x) = (\varphi|\xi_x)$ for $\varphi \in C^1(M,\mathbb{R})$. The assignment $x \mapsto \xi_x$ is called a *vector field* on M.

We set $T^1(M) = \bigcup_{x\in M} T^1(M,x)$. It can be given the structure of a C^0 manifold as follows. If $(\mathcal{V},\Phi)$ is a chart on M and $x \in \mathcal{V}$ then $(\partial_i)_{i=1}^d$ (their dependence on x is suppressed in this notation) forms a basis of $T^1(M,x)$. Expanding $\xi_x = \Sigma b^k\partial_k$ then the coordinates b^k are functions of ξ_x, so more precisely $\xi_x = \Sigma b^k(\xi_x)\partial_k$, and we can use $(\Phi\pi,b)$ as a chart map on $T^1(\mathcal{V}) = \bigcup_{x\in\mathcal{V}} T^1(M,x)$ (inducing a topology at the same time) into $\mathbb{R}^d\times\mathbb{R}^d$ where $\pi(\xi_x) = x$ and $b(\xi_x) = (b^1(\xi_x), b^2(\xi_x),\ldots, b^d(\xi_x))$. A vector field is then simply a C^0 map $\xi:M \to T^1(M)$ such that $\pi\circ\xi = id_M$. Note that $\pi: T^1(M) \to M$ is C^0. Thus we have an identification between vector fields and first order differential operators without zero-th order term on M.

$T^1(M)$ is a particular instance of a vector bundle over M. In general we call a triple $(\mathbb{V},\pi,B)$ a *vector bundle* $\mathbb{V}$ *over the base space* B *with projection* π if: V and B are topological spaces, $\pi:\mathbb{V} \to B$ is a continuous surjection, each fiber $F_x := \pi^{-1}(x)$ has a vector space structure (isomorphic to some fixed space E, say), and about each $v \in \mathbb{V}$ there is an open set $\mathcal{V}$ which is homeomorphic under Ψ, say, to the product $E \times \pi\mathcal{V}$ with $\Psi|_{F_x} : F_x \to E$ a linear isomorphism for each $x \in \pi\mathcal{V}$. A *section* of $\mathbb{V}$ is a continuous map $\xi : B \to \mathbb{V}$ such that $\pi \circ \xi = id_B$. If B has a differential structure of a manifold, the definition may be amended to include smoothness assumptions on π and Ψ as well if appropriate in which case V becomes a manifold. If $\Phi : \pi\mathcal{V} \to \mathcal{V}$ is a chart on M, $(id_E \times \Phi) \circ \Psi$ is one on $\mathbb{V}$. (The reason for introducing this abstract notion at this point is that $T^1(M)$ is only the first of several vector bundles which will be introduced in this section.) The zero section ($x \mapsto$ origin of $\pi^{-1}(x)$) allows us to identify the base B as a subspace of $\mathbb{V}$. A map $\mathbb{L} : \mathbb{V} \to \mathbb{W}$ between two vector bundles $(\mathbb{V}, \pi_B, B)$, $(\mathbb{W}, \pi_C, C)$ is called a *vector bundle map* or *morphism* if it is a linear map of the fiber over x into the fiber over $\mathbb{L}(x)$ for each $x \in M$: $\mathbb{L}|\pi_B^{-1}(x) : \pi_B^{-1}(x) \to \pi_C^{-1}(x)$.

Suppose now that M is a C^2 manifold. We endow $C^2(M,\mathbb{R})$ with the complete metrizable topology of uniform convergence of functions and their first and second derivatives on compact sets. For each $x \in M$ define $T^2(M,x)$ to be the subset of $C^2(M,\mathbb{R})^*$ (the dual of C^2) consisting of elements L_x which have their supports contained in $\{x\}$ (i.e. if $\varphi \in C^2$ and $\text{supp}\varphi \cap \{x\} = \phi$ then $(\varphi|L_x) \equiv (\varphi, L_x)_2 := L_x\varphi = 0$) and such that $(1|L_x) = 0$. Clearly $T^1(M,x) \subset T^2(M,x)$.

As an example, if $(\mathcal{V},\Phi)$ is a chart about $x \in M$ then the partial derivatives $\partial_i\partial_j \in T^2(M,x)$, $1 \leq i,j \leq d = \dim M$, where $\partial_i\partial_j = \frac{\partial^2}{\partial x_i \partial x_j}(\varphi|_{\mathcal{V}} \circ \Phi^{-1})|_{\Phi(x)}$, the second partial derivative taken in the usual sense. It can be shown that if $L_x \in T^2(M,x)$ then $L_x = \Sigma b^k\partial_k + \frac{1}{2}\Sigma a^{ij}\partial_i\partial_j$ (with $a^{ij} = a^{ji}$) where necessarily $b^k = (\alpha[\Phi_k - \Phi_k(x)]|L_x)$ and $a^{ij} = (\alpha[\Phi_i - \Phi_i(x)][\Phi_j - \Phi_j(x)]|L_x)$ for $\alpha \in C^2(M)$ with $\operatorname{supp}\alpha \subset \mathcal{V}$ and $\alpha = 1$ on a neighbourhood of x, and where Φ_k is the k-th Euclidean coordinate of Φ. In particular $(\partial_k, \partial_{ij})_{\substack{1\leq k\leq d \\ 1\leq i\leq j\leq d}}$ forms a basis of $T^2(M,x)$ which therefore has dimension $d+d(d+1)/2$.

We set $T^2(M) = \bigcup_{x\in M} T^2(M,x)$. It can be given the structure of a C^0 manifold as follows. If $(\mathcal{V},\Phi)$ is a chart on M and $x \in \mathcal{V}$ then $(\Phi\circ\pi, b, a)$ is a chart map on $T^2(\mathcal{V}) = \bigcup_{x\in\mathcal{V}} T^2(M,x)$ (inducing a topology at the same time) where $\pi : T^2(M) \to M$ is given by $\pi(L_x) = x$, and $b = b(L_x)$, $a = a(L_x)$ are the $d+d(d+1)/2$ coordinates of L_x with respect to the basis $(\partial_k, \partial_i\partial_j)_{\substack{1\leq k\leq d \\ 1\leq i\leq j\leq d}}$. Note that $\pi : T^2(M) \to M$ is C^0, rendering $T^2(M)$ a C^0 vector bundle over M.

Recall that a second order differential operator without zero-th order term is a continuous linear map

$L:C^2(M,\mathbb{R}) \to C^0(M,\mathbb{R})$ which is local and such that $L1 = 0$. If L is such an operator then it induces a continuous section $x \mapsto L_x$ of $T^2(M)$ given by $(\varphi|L_x) = (L\varphi)(x)$. Conversely this equation also defines such an operator, starting with a continuous section of $T^2(M)$.

In the case where M is an open subset of E, a finite dimensional real vector space, we can and will identify $T^2(M,x)$ with $E \oplus (E \odot E)$ in the following way. The map $E\times E \to T^2(M,x)$ given by $(v,w) \mapsto \partial_v\partial_w$ is symmetric and bilinear; it thus lifts to linear map of $E\odot E \to T^2(M,x)$ such that $v\odot w \mapsto \partial_v\partial_w$. More generally the map of $E\oplus(E\times E) \to T^2(M,x)$ given by $(u,v,w) \to \partial_u+\partial_v\partial_w$ induces a linear map of $E\oplus(E\odot E) \to T^2(M,x)$ such that $u\oplus(v\odot w) \mapsto \partial_u+\partial_v\partial_w$. It is easy to check that the image of the first map, on $E\oplus(E\odot E)$, generates $T^2(M,x)$; so by a dimension count, the isomorphism is established. If $(e_i)_{i=1}^d$ is a basis of E then under this isomorphism we have the correspondences: $e_k \leftrightarrow \partial_k$ and $e_i \odot e_j \leftrightarrow \partial_i\partial_j$. We shall denote elements of $T^2(M,x)$, in this case, by column vectors: $L_x = \begin{pmatrix} L_1 \\ L_2 \end{pmatrix}$ with $L_1 \in E$, $L_2 \in E\odot E$.

In the general manifold setting we cannot split $T^2(M,x)$ into direct summands, one of which is $T^1(M,x)$, in a canonical way; that is except locally since the previous prescription is heavily chart-dependent: in a change of charts a purely second order term usually transforms to one which includes a first order part. However the situation is better for the quotient $T^2(M,x)/T^1(M,x)$; it is canonically isomorphic to $T^1(M,x) \odot T^1(M,x)$ in a way which we shall now describe. Given $\xi_x, \eta_x \in T^1(M,x)$ extend them arbitrarily to C^1 vector fields ξ, η on M and view them as first order differential operators. Let $L = \xi\eta$ i.e. $L\varphi := \xi(\eta(\varphi))$; then L is a second order differential operator without constant term, so that $L_x \in T^2(M,x)$. Then $(\xi_x, \eta_x) \mapsto L_x (\mathrm{mod}\, T^1(M,x))$ is a symmetric bilinear map of $T^1(M,x) \times T^1(M,x) \to T^2(M,x)/T^1(M,x)$ which is independent of the extensions and which then lifts to a linear map of $T^1(M,x) \odot T^1(M,x) \to T^2(M,x)/T^1(M,x)$. Indeed, in any chart:

$$L\varphi = \xi(\Sigma\eta^i\partial_i\varphi) = \Sigma\xi^j\partial_j(\eta^i\partial_i\varphi) = \Sigma\xi^i\eta^i\partial_i\partial_j\varphi + \Sigma\xi^j(\partial_j\eta^i)\partial_i\varphi .$$

Therefore $L_x \equiv \Sigma\xi^j_x\eta^i_x\partial_i\partial_j \; (\mathrm{mod}\, T^1(M,x))$, so that all our claims are easily checked. Also it is easy to check that our intrinsic map is bijective. Thus we have an identification between the vector bundles $T^2(M)/T^1(M)$ and $T^1(M) \odot T^1(M)$ (whose fibers are $T^2(M,x)/T^1(M,x)$ and $T^1(M,x) \odot T^1(M,x)$ respectively with the obvious projections π) given by the map just described on the fibers; it is obviously a vector bundle isomorphism.

3. SECOND ORDER DIFFERENTIAL GEOMETRY: $T^{*1}(M)$ AND $T^{*2}(M)$

We now turn our attention to matters of a dual nature. Let M be a C^2 manifold and for $x \in M$ define $C^2_{(k)}(M;x)$, $k=0,1,2$ to be the subspace of $C^2(M)$ whose members vanish as well as their derivatives (in some and hence any chart) up to order k at x. We define $T^{*1}(M,x) = C^2_{(0)}(M;x)/C^2_{(1)}(M;x)$ and $T^{*2}(M,x) = C^2_{(0)}(M;x)/C^2_{(2)}(M;x)$. Their significance can be explained as follows. Define the maps $\rho_1 : C^2_{(0)}(M;x) \to T^1(M,x)^*$ and $\rho_2 : C^2_{(0)}(M;x) \to T^2(M;x)^*$ (* denoting the dual) by

$$\rho_1(\varphi)(\xi_x) = (\varphi|\xi_x), \quad \xi_x \in T^1(M,x)$$

$$\rho_2(\varphi)(L_x) = (\varphi|L_x), \quad L_x \in T^2(M,x) .$$

By looking at things in a chart it is not hard to see that ρ_1 and ρ_2 are surjective (it amounts to being able to prescribe the first and second derivatives of a quadratic polynomial at a fixed point). Also it is clear (again via a chart) that the kernels of ρ_1 and ρ_2 are $C^2_{(1)}(M;x)$ and $C^2_{(2)}(M;x)$ respectively, so that $T^{*1}(M,x) \simeq T^1(M,x)^*$ and $T^{*2}(M,x) \simeq T^2(M,x)^*$. Since the isomorphism is intrinsic we shall regard it as an identification. Denoting the equivalence class of $\varphi \in C^2_{(0)}(M;x)$ in $T^{*1}(M,x)$ and $T^{*2}(M,x)$ by $D^1\varphi(x)$ and $D^2\varphi(x)$ respectively, we can write the pairings as:

$$(D^1\varphi(x)|\xi_x)_{T^{*1},T^1} = (\varphi|\xi_x)_1, \quad \xi_x \in T^1(M,x)$$

$$(D^2\varphi(x)|L_x)_{T^{*2},T^2} = (\varphi|L_x)_2, \quad L_x \in T^2(M,x) .$$

(Strictly speaking we should always index the pairings on the left and right hand sides differently; but we shan't.) For general $\varphi \in C^2(M)$ we set $D^{(k)}\varphi(x) = D^{(k)}[\varphi-\varphi(x)](x)$, $k=1,2$.

Note that $T^{*1}(M,x)$ is a quotient of $T^{*2}(M,x)$; this can be seen in two ways. Firstly we have $C^2_{(0)}(M;x)/C^2_{(1)}(M;x) \simeq [C^2_{(0)}(M;x)/C^2_{(2)}(M;x)]/[C^2_{(1)}(M;x)/C^2_{(2)}(M;x)]$. Secondly, denoting the injection of $T^1(M,x) \hookrightarrow T^2(M,x)$ by j, we have the surjective adjoint $j^*:T^{*2}(M,x) \to T^{*1}(M,x)$.

Recall that when M was an open subset of a finite dimensional real vector space E we made the identification $T^2(M,x) = E \oplus (E\odot E)$ for all $x \in M$. It would then seem natural to identify $T^2(M,x)^*$ with $E^* \oplus \mathcal{L}_{2,sym}(E\times E)$, $\mathcal{L}_{2,sym}(E\times E)$ being the vector space of real valued symmetric bilinear maps on E×E, by writing the elements of the latter as row vectors (ℓ_1,ℓ_2) which operate on the column vectors $\binom{L_1}{L_2}$ of $T^2(M,x)$ through matrix multiplication:

$$(\ell_1 \; \ell_2)\binom{L_1}{L_2} = \ell_1 L_1 + \ell_2 L_2 .$$

We can reconcile this with the identification of $T^2(M,x)^*$ with $T^{*2}(M,x)$ as follows. We let the matrix-type identification, as discussed above, be denoted by $i: E^* \oplus \mathcal{L}_{2,sym}(E\times E) \simeq [E \oplus (E\odot E)]^*$, $\nu: E\oplus(E\odot E) \simeq T^2(M,x)$ be the previously encountered identification such that $\nu(u, v\odot w) = \partial_u + \partial_v\partial_w$, and $\bar{\rho}_2: T^{*2}(M,x) \simeq T^2(M,x)^*$ be as described in the beginning of this section: $\bar{\rho}_2(D^2\varphi(x)) = (\varphi|\cdot_x)$. Define $\sigma: C^2_{(0)}(M,x) \to E^* \oplus \mathcal{L}_{2,sym}(E\times E)$ by $\sigma(\varphi) = (\varphi'(x), \varphi''(x))$. Then σ is surjective with kernel $C^2_{(2)}(M;x)$ and thus induces an isomorphism $\bar{\sigma}: T^{*2}(M,x) \simeq E^* \oplus \mathcal{L}_{2,sym}(E\times E)$. The reconciliation is precisely the commutivity of the following diagram:

$$\begin{array}{ccc} T^{*2}(M,x) & \xrightarrow{\ \bar{\sigma}\ } & E^*\oplus\mathcal{L}_{2,sym}(E\times E) \\ \downarrow \bar{\rho}_2 & & \downarrow i \\ T^2(M,x)^* & \xrightarrow[\ \nu^*\ ]{} & [E\oplus(E\odot E)]^* \end{array}$$

Now

$$i\circ\bar{\sigma}(D^2\varphi(x))\binom{u}{v\odot w} = \varphi'(x)\cdot u + \varphi''(x)(v,w)$$

$$\nu^*\circ\bar{\rho}_2(D^2\varphi(x))\binom{u}{v\odot w} = (\varphi|[\partial_u+\partial_v\partial_w]_x)$$

$$= \varphi'(x)\cdot u + \varphi'(x)(v,w)$$

and by linearity we have the commutativity on all of $E\oplus(E\odot E)$.

Thus by a harmless abuse of notation whereby we write simply $D^2\varphi(x)$ in place of $\bar{\sigma}(D^2\varphi(x))$ we can write formulas such as:

$$D^2\varphi(x) = (\varphi'(x), \varphi''(x))$$

$$D^2\varphi(x)\xi_x = (\varphi|\xi_x) = \varphi'(x)\cdot\xi_x$$

$$D^2\varphi(x)(\xi_x \odot \eta_x) = \varphi''(\xi_x, \eta_x) = \partial_\xi \partial_\eta \varphi(x)$$

$$D^2\varphi(x)L_x = (D^2\varphi(x)|L_x) = (\varphi|L_x).$$

Returning to the general manifold setting, if $(\mathcal{V}, \Phi)$ is a chart on M and $(\Phi_k)_{k=1}^d$ are the coordinate functions, then $(D^1\Phi_k(x), D^2[\Phi_i\Phi_j](x))_{\substack{1\le k\le d \\ 1\le i\le j\le d}}$ form the dual basis of [illegible],x) to $(\partial_k, \partial_i\partial_j)_{\substack{1\le k\le d \\ 1\le i\le j\le d}}$ at each $x \in \mathcal{V}$. The linear coordinates of an element of $T^{*2}(M,x)$, with respect to the former basis, along with Φ constitute a chart on $T^{*2}(\mathcal{V}) := \bigcup_{x\in\mathcal{V}} T^{*2}(M,x)$ (in a way similar to that on $T^2(M)$) rendering $T^{*2}(M) := \bigcup_{x\in M} T^{*2}(M,x)$ a $d+(d+d(d+1)/2)$ dimensional manifold and moreover a vector bundle over M with projection π: $D^2\varphi(x) \mapsto x$.

4. TRANSFORMATIONS

If M and N are C^2 manifolds and $\Phi: M \to N$ is C^2, then Φ induces linear mapping $\overset{2}{\Phi}: T^2(M,x) \to T^2(N,\Phi(x))$ for each $x \in M$ which is defined by $(\varphi|\overset{2}{\Phi}L_x) = (\varphi\circ\Phi|L_x)$ for all $L_x \in T^2(M,x)$ and $\varphi \in C^2(N)$. Clearly $\overset{2}{\Phi}(T^1(M,x)) \subset T^1(N,\Phi(x))$ and we denote the restriction of $\overset{2}{\Phi}$ to $T^1(M,x)$ by $\overset{1}{\Phi}$ (which could have also been defined directly by $(\varphi|\overset{1}{\Phi}\xi_x) = (\varphi\circ\Phi|\xi_x)$ for all $\xi_x \in T^1(M,x)$ and $\varphi \in C^1(N)$ if all our ingredients were only C^1).

Dually $\overset{2}{\Phi}{}^*_x : T^{*2}(N,\Phi(x)) \to T^{*2}(M,x)$ is given by $\overset{2}{\Phi}{}^*_x D^2\varphi(\Phi(x)) := D^2[\Phi^*\varphi](x) \equiv D^2[\varphi\circ\Phi](x)$ so that $(\overset{2}{\Phi}{}^*_x D^2\varphi(\Phi(x))|L_x) = ([D^2\varphi](\Phi(x))|[\overset{2}{\Phi}L_x]_{(x)})$ for all $\varphi \in C^2(N)$, $L_x \in T^2(M,x)$. A similar definition and result hold for $\overset{1}{\Phi}{}^*_x$. Note that to check that these maps are well defined one must show that the mapping of $C^2_{(0)}(N,\Phi(x)) \to T^{*2}(M,x)$ given by $\varphi \to D^2[\varphi\circ\Phi](x)$ has $C^2_{(2)}(N;\Phi(x))$ contained in its kernel. We will be doing a calculation of this sort shortly for another reason and so will not reproduce it here.

Note that $\overset{1}{\Phi}$ and $\overset{2}{\Phi}$ are both vector bundle mappings and since $\overset{1}{\Phi}(T^1(M)) \subset T^1(N)$, $\overset{1}{\Phi} \odot \overset{1}{\Phi} : T^1(M)\odot T^1(M) \to T^1(N)\odot T^1(N)$ and we have, by an earlier studied isomorphism, the diagram

$$\begin{array}{ccc} T^2(M)/T^1(M) & \to & T^2(N)/T^1(N) \\ \| & & \| \\ T^1(M)\odot T^1(M) & \to & T^1(N)\odot T^1(N) \end{array}$$

which is commutative.

We now study the representations of $\overset{2}{\Phi}$ and $\overset{2}{\Phi}{}^*$ when M and N are open subsets of finite dimensional real vector spaces E and F respectively, in light of the identifications made in this case. If $\varphi \in C^2(N)$, then $(\varphi|[\overset{2}{\Phi}L_x]_{\Phi(x)}) = (\varphi\circ\Phi|L_x) =$

$D^2[\varphi\circ\Phi](x)\cdot L_x$ for all $L_x \in T^2(M,x)$. Now, $D^2[\varphi\circ\Phi](x) = ([\varphi\circ\Phi]'(x),[\varphi\circ\Phi]''(x)) = (\varphi'(\Phi(x))\Phi'(x),\varphi''(\Phi(x))[\Phi'(x)\odot\Phi'(x)]+ \varphi'(\Phi(x))\Phi''(x))$. Therefore since $(\varphi|[\overset{2}{\Phi} L_x]_{\Phi(x)}) = [D^2\varphi](\Phi(x)).([\overset{2}{\Phi}L_x]_{\Phi(x)})$ by our definition, we see that $\overset{2}{\Phi}$ is represented by left multiplication by the matrix

$$\overset{2}{\underline{\Phi}} = \begin{pmatrix} \Phi'(x) & \Phi''(x) \\ 0 & \Phi'(x) \odot \Phi'(x) \end{pmatrix}$$

and that $\overset{2}{\Phi}{}^*$ is represented by right multiplication by the same matrix:

$$\overset{2}{\Phi}L_x = \overset{2}{\underline{\Phi}}\binom{L_1}{L_2}$$

$$[\overset{2}{\Phi}{}^*D^2\varphi](\Phi(x)) = [D^2\varphi](\Phi(x))\overset{2}{\underline{\Phi}} .$$

In closing this section, we note that if $x:\mathbb{R} \to M$ is a C^2 curve, then $\dot{x} = \overset{1}{x}:R \to T^1(M)$ and $\overset{2}{\underline{x}}:R\oplus(R\cdot R)\to T^2(M)$ at each instant $t \in \mathbb{R}$, and that the complete acceleration $\underline{\ddot{x}}$ is related to $\overset{2}{x}$ by $\underline{\ddot{x}} = \overset{2}{\underline{x}}(1\odot 1)$.

5. INTEGRATION ALONG A CONTINUOUS SEMIMARTINGALE

In this section we will consider a stochastic analogue of integration of differential 1-forms along smooth paths in a manifold. Recall that if $\gamma:\mathbb{R}_+ \to M$ is a C^1 curve and η a C^0 1-form on M (i.e. η is a continuous section of

$T^{*1}(M))$, then we define the integral $\int_{\gamma_0^t} \eta$ by

$$\int_0^t (\eta(\gamma(s))|\dot{\gamma}(s))ds.$$

In particular, if $\eta = d\varphi$ (or $D^1\varphi$ in our notation) where $\varphi \in C^1(M)$, then

$$\int_{\gamma_0^t} \eta = \int_{\gamma_0^t} d\varphi = \int_0^t (d\varphi(\gamma(s))|\dot{\gamma}(s))ds = \int_0^t \frac{d}{ds}(\varphi\circ\gamma)(s)ds$$
$$= \varphi(\gamma(t))-\varphi(\gamma(0))$$

which is the so-called property of exactness. Conversely $\dot{\gamma}(s)$ is the unique vector field $\xi(s)$ along γ such that $\int_0^t(d\varphi(\gamma(s))|\xi(s))ds = \varphi(\gamma(t))-\varphi(\gamma(0))$ for all $\varphi \in C^1(M)$.

For future reference by analogy we denote $\int_{\gamma_0^t} \eta$ also by $(\eta\cdot\gamma)_t$, and more generally any indefinite integration by a dot as well. For instance if $\alpha:\mathbb{R}_+ \to \mathbb{R}$ is continuous then $\int_0^t \alpha(s)d(\eta\cdot\gamma)_s = \int_{\gamma_0^t} \alpha\eta$ and this equation may be expressed briefly as $\alpha\cdot(\eta\cdot\gamma) = (\alpha\eta)\cdot\gamma$, where the dot outside the parentheses on the left hand side is an indefinite Stieltjes integration.

Suppose now that ξ is a continuous vector field on M and that γ satisfies the differential equation $\dot{\gamma}(t) = \xi_{\gamma(t)}$. Then for any 1-form η, we have that

$$\int_{\gamma_0^t} \eta = \int_0^t \langle\eta(\gamma(s))|\dot{\gamma}(s)) \, ds = \int_0^t (\eta(\gamma(s))|\xi_{\gamma(s)}) \, ds .$$

Conversely, if the first and last integrals above are equal for all 1-forms η and all t then γ is a solution to the differential equation. Actually it suffices to have the equality for η of the form $\eta = d\varphi$ for $\varphi \in C^1(M)$, whereupon we obtain $\int_0^t (d\varphi(\gamma(s))|\xi_{\gamma(s)})ds = \varphi(\gamma(t))-\varphi(\gamma(0))$.

Thus we see that the roles of the vector field $\dot{\gamma}(t)$ in integration and differential equations can be cast (in fact characterized) in such a way that no derivatives appear (at least superficially). In other words the existence of the "infinitesimal" quantity $\dot{\gamma}(t)$ can be viewed equivalently via its role as an indefinite integrator. More precisely, we state the following proposition, after giving a definition.

Definition. Let $\gamma \in C^1(\mathbb{R},M)$ and write $T^{*1}(M;\gamma)$ for the set of continuous mappings $\eta:\mathbb{R}_+ \to T^{*1}(M)$ such that $\eta(t) \in T^{*1}(M,\gamma(t))$ for each $t \in \mathbb{R}_+$ i.e. $\pi\circ\eta = \gamma$; $T^{*1}(M;\gamma)$ becomes a module over $C^0(\mathbb{R}_+,\mathbb{R})$ by the usual pointwise scalar multiplication. $C^1(\mathbb{R}_+,\mathbb{R})$ is a module over $C^0(\mathbb{R}_+,\mathbb{R})$ via Stieltjes integration: $(\alpha\cdot\beta)_t := \int_0^t\alpha(s)\beta'(s)ds$ for $\alpha \in C^0(\mathbb{R}_+,\mathbb{R})$, $\beta \in C^1(\mathbb{R}_+,\mathbb{R})$.

Proposition. There exists a unique map: $T^{*1}(M;\gamma) \to C^1(\mathbb{R}_+,\mathbb{R})$ which is denoted by $\eta \mapsto \eta\cdot\gamma$, which is linear in the sense that for $\alpha \in C^0(\mathbb{R}_+,\mathbb{R})$ we have $\alpha\cdot(\eta\cdot\gamma) = (\alpha\eta)\cdot\gamma$, and such that $d\varphi(\gamma)\cdot\gamma = \varphi(\gamma)-\varphi(\gamma(0))$ for all $\varphi \in C^1(M)$.

In fact from the discussion leading up to this proposition it is clear that this map is given by $(\eta\cdot\gamma)_t = \int_0^t (\eta(s)|\dot{\gamma}(s))\,ds$.

Turning now from the smooth deterministic setting to the stochastic setting, we have seen in the orientation section that the formal differential $d\underline{X}_t$ of a complete semimartingale (in a chart) transforms as a second order tangent vector. Instead of trying to find a rigorous definition for the infinitesimal object $d\underline{X}_t$, we shall find an interpretation of it as an indefinite integrator of second order cotangent processes along X i.e. we shall prove a second order analogue of the previous proposition with Itô's formula supplying the exactness property.

<u>Definition.</u> Let X be a continuous M-semimartingale We denote by $T^{*2}(M;X)$ the set of optional processes $J:\bar{R}_+\times\Omega \to T^{*2}(M)$ such that $J(t,\omega) \in T^{*2}(M,X(t,\omega))$ for $\mathbb{P}$-a.e. ω; i.e. $\pi\circ J_t = X_t$ almost surely.

In the next theorem we are going to give a meaning to $\int_{]0,t]} (J_s|d\underline{X}_s)$, as a real valued semimartingale, for $J \in T^{*2}(M;X)$. There are two ways of proceeding. We can restrict attention to only prelocally bounded integrands (this means that if $\bar{K}_n \subset K_{n+1}$ are compact sets whose union is M and we define $T_n = \inf\{t:X_t \notin K_n\}$ then $T_n\uparrow\uparrow+\infty$ and in $[0,T_n[$, $X_t \in K_n$, a compact set, on which there is a sense of boundedness of J through the use of charts; and this notion is independent of the choice of charts) or we can make no restrictions on J and interpret the integral as a formal semimartingale. We shall choose the latter approach since it makes for smoother sailing in the middle of any proof, our not having to check for integrability at every turn.

Theorem. Let X be a continuous M-semimartingale. Then there exists a unique map of $T^{*2}(M;X) \to \mathrm{Opt}\mathcal{S}M_0^c$, which is denoted by either $J \mapsto J\cdot\underline{X}$ or $\int_{]0,t]} (J_s|d\underline{X}_s)$, which satisfies the following two properties:

1) Opt-linearity: $(\alpha J)\circ\underline{X} = \alpha\cdot(J.\underline{X})$ for all $\alpha \in \mathrm{Opt}$ (i.e. α a real-valued optional process)

2) Exactness: for all $\varphi \in C^2(M)$,

$[D^2\varphi(X)]\cdot\underline{X} = \varphi(X)-\varphi(X_0)$.

Proof. The proof is based upon the following simple observation from algebra. If $\mathcal{A}$ and $\mathcal{B}$ are two modules over the same ring $\mathcal{R}$, $\mathcal{E}$ is a subset of $\mathcal{A}$, and $u:\mathcal{E}\to\mathcal{B}$, then u extends in a unique way to a linear map (module morphism) $\bar{u}:\mathcal{A}\to\mathcal{B}$ iff

(i) $\mathcal{E}$ generates $\mathcal{A}$: each $a \in \mathcal{A}$ admits a decomposition

$$a = \sum_{\text{finite}} \alpha_\ell e_\ell,\quad \alpha_\ell \in \mathcal{R},\quad e_\ell \in \mathcal{E},$$

(ii) $\Sigma\alpha_\ell e_\ell = 0$ implies $\Sigma\alpha_\ell u(e_\ell) = 0$.

In our situation we will be applying this to $\mathcal{R}$ = Opt, $\mathcal{A} = T^{*2}(M;X)$, $\mathcal{B} = \mathrm{Opt}SM_0^c$, $\mathcal{E} = \{D^2\varphi(X):\varphi \in C^2(M)\}$, and $u:D^2\varphi(X) \mapsto \varphi(X)-\varphi(X_0)$. We will give several verifications of property (ii), one at present and the others in an appendix.

Concerning property (i), we must show that if $J \in T^{*2}(M;X)$ then it admits a decomposition $\sum_{\text{finite}} \alpha_\ell D^2\varphi_\ell(X)$ where $\alpha_\ell \in$ Opt and $\varphi_\ell \in C^2(M)$. Embed $M \hookrightarrow E$ a 2d-dimensional real vector space where d = dimM. For each $x \in M$, $T^{*2}(E,x)$ is generated by the $2d+2d(2d+1)/2 = d(2d+3)$ elements $D^2\psi(x)$ where ψ is of the form $y = (y_1,\dots,y_{2d}) \mapsto y_k$, $k=1,2,3,\dots,2d$, or $y \mapsto y_iy_j$, $1 \le i \le j \le 2d$. Since every C^2 function on M can be extended to an element of $C^2(E)$, it is easy to see that $T^{*2}(M,x)$ is generated by the cotangent vectors $D^2\varphi(x)$ where the φ's are the restrictions of the ψ's to M. Choose $d+d(d+1)/2$ of these cotangent vectors which are linearly independent, forming a basis of $T^{*2}(M,x)$. By continuity they will remain linearly independent in an M-neighbourhood V of x. Denote the original collection of $D^2\varphi(x)$'s by $(D^2\varphi_\ell(x))_{\ell\in L}$, where $L = \{k,(i,j):1 \le k \le 2d,\ 1 \le i \le j \le 2d\}$, and the choice of linearly independent ones by $(D^2\varphi_\ell(x))_{\ell\in L'}$; cardinality of $L' = d+d(d+1)/2$. Repeat this construction (or selection) to obtain such a basis on each member of an open covering $(V_n)_{n\in N}$ of M. On $X^{-1}(V_n)$, $J = \sum_{\ell\in L_n'} \alpha_{\ell,n} D^2\varphi_\ell(X)$

where for fixed $\omega, \alpha_{\ell,n}(\cdot,\omega)$ is continuous. Letting $V_n' = V_n \setminus V_{n-1}$ $(V_0 = \phi)$ for $n \geq 1$ and defining $\alpha_\ell = \begin{cases} \alpha_{\ell,n}, & \text{for } \ell \in L_n' \\ 0, & \text{for } \ell \notin L_n' \end{cases}$ on $X^{-1}(V_n')$ yields $\alpha_\ell \in \text{Opt}$; moreover for fixed ω, $\alpha_\ell(.,\omega)$ is a Borel function. Clearly $J = \sum_{\ell \in L} \alpha_\ell D^2\varphi_\ell(X)$.

Concerning (ii), we must show that $\Sigma\alpha_\ell D^2\varphi_\ell(X) = 0$ implies that $0 = \Sigma\alpha_\ell \cdot (\varphi_\ell(X) - \varphi_\ell(X_0))$ which is the same as $0 = \Sigma\alpha_\ell \cdot \varphi_\ell(X)$. To this end it suffices to show that $\Sigma\alpha_\ell \cdot \varphi_\ell(X) \underset{A_n}{\sim} 0$ where the A_n are open and $\bigcup_n A_n = \bar{R}_+ \times \Omega$. Let $(V_n, \Phi_n)_{n\in N}$ be an atlas on M and $(V_n')_{n\in N}$ be a locally finite refinement of $(V_n)_{n\in N}$ such that for each n there exists an m with $\bar{V}_n' \subset V_m$. Extend $\Phi_m|_{V_n'}$ in a C^2 fashion to all of M and call the extension $\bar{\Phi}_n$. Define $A_n = X^{-1}(V_n')$ and set $Y_n = \bar{\Phi}_n(X) \in \mathcal{SM}^c$. On A_n, $X = \Phi_n^{-1}(Y_n)$; therefore $\varphi_\ell(X) = \varphi_\ell \circ \Phi_n^{-1}(Y_n)$. Extend $\Phi_n^{-1}|_{\Phi_n(V_n')}$ to $\Psi_n \in C^2(E,M)$ and denote $\varphi_\ell \circ \Psi_n$ by $\psi_{\ell,n}$. Thus on $A_n: \varphi_\ell(X) = \psi_{\ell,n}(Y_n)$ and also $\Sigma\alpha_\ell D^2\varphi_\ell(\Psi_n(Y_n)) = \Sigma\alpha_\ell D^2\varphi_\ell(X) = 0$. Therefore on A_n

$$
\begin{aligned}
0 &= [\overset{2}{\Psi}{}_n^*\{\Sigma\alpha_\ell D^2\varphi_\ell(\Psi_n(Y_n))\}](Y_n) && (\overset{2}{\Psi}{}_n^*: T^{*2}(M,\Psi_n(Y_n)) \to T^{*2}(E,Y_n); \\
&= \Sigma\alpha_\ell([\overset{2}{\Psi}{}_n^*\{D^2\varphi_\ell(\Psi_n(Y_n))\}](Y_n)) && \text{no room left on } \overset{2}{\Psi}{}_n^* \text{ to index} \\
&= \Sigma\alpha_\ell D^2(\varphi_\ell \circ \Psi_n)(Y_n) && \text{by } Y_n) \\
&= \Sigma\alpha_\ell D^2\psi_{\ell,n}(Y_n) .
\end{aligned}
$$

Finally, we calculate,

$\Sigma\alpha_\ell \cdot \varphi_\ell(X) \underset{A_n}{\sim} \Sigma\alpha_\ell \cdot \psi_{\ell,n}(Y_n)$ (by a theorem of equivalence since $\varphi_\ell(X) = \psi_{\ell,n}(Y_n)$ on A_n)

$\underset{A_n}{\sim} \Sigma\alpha_\ell \cdot (D^2\psi_{\ell,n}(Y_n)\cdot \underline{Y}_n)$ (by Itô's formula; recall $\underline{Y}_n = \begin{pmatrix} Y_n \\ \frac{1}{2}[Y_n,Y_n] \end{pmatrix}$)

$\underset{A_n}{\sim} (\Sigma[\alpha_\ell D^2\psi_{\ell,n}(Y_n)])\cdot \underline{Y}_n$ (equality actually)

$\underset{A_n}{\sim} 0$ (by a theorem of equivalence since the sum is 0 on A_n by the previous calculation). □

<u>Remark</u>. In the vectorial case where $J = (J_1,J_2)$ and $\underline{X} = \begin{pmatrix} X \\ \frac{1}{2}[X,X] \end{pmatrix}$ the map $J \mapsto J\cdot \underline{X}$ is then given by the "matrix product" $J_1\cdot X + \frac{1}{2}J_2\cdot [X,X]$ since this map is Opt-linear and by Itô's formula: $D^2\varphi(X) = (\varphi'(X),\varphi''(X))) \mapsto \varphi'(X)\cdot X + \frac{1}{2}\varphi''(X)\cdot [X,X] = \varphi(X)-\varphi(X_0)$.

We can now give a precise and rigorous interpretation of the behaviour of $d\underline{X}_t$, under a C^2 transformation Φ, as a second order tangent vector. If M and N are C^2 manifolds, $\Phi \in C^2(M,N)$, and X is a continuous M-semimartingale then $Y := \Phi(X)$ is a continuous N-semimartingale. Heuristically,

$d\underline{X}_t \overset{\overset{2}{\Phi}}{\mapsto} d\underline{Y}_t$; rigorously we can show that if $J \in T^{*2}(N,Y)$ then $J\cdot\underline{Y} = (\overset{2}{\Phi}{}^*_X J)\cdot\underline{X}$, where we recall that if $y = \Phi(x)$ then $\overset{2}{\Phi}{}^*_x : T^{*2}(N,y) \to T^{*2}(M,x)$ by $\overset{2}{\Phi}{}^*_x(D^2\varphi(y)) = D^2(\varphi\circ\Phi)(x)$ for $\varphi \in C^2(N)$. Since $T^{*2}(N;Y)$ is generated by $\mathcal{E} = \{D^2\varphi(Y): \varphi \in C^2(N)\}$ it suffices by Opt-linearity to verify our claim for $J \in \mathcal{E}$. In this case $J\cdot\underline{Y} = D^2\varphi(Y)\cdot\underline{Y} = \varphi(Y)-\varphi(Y_0) = \varphi\circ\Phi(X)-\varphi\circ\Phi(X_0)$ and $(\overset{2}{\Phi}{}^*_X J)\cdot\underline{X} = [\overset{2}{\Phi}{}^*_X D^2\varphi(Y)]\cdot\underline{X} = D^2(\varphi\circ\Phi)(X)\cdot\underline{X} = \varphi\circ\Phi(X)-\varphi\circ\Phi(X_0)$. In an alternate notation we have shown that $\int_0^t (J_s|d(\Phi(X))_s) = \int_0^t (\overset{2}{\Phi}{}^*_{X_s} J_s|dX_s)$.

In particular we can apply this result to the situation $M \overset{j}{\hookrightarrow} N$, M a submanifold of N. For $J \in T^{*2}(M;X)$ and any $J' \in T^{*2}(N;X)$ such that $\overset{2}{j}{}^*J' = J$ (there always exists such J' since every $\varphi \in C^2(M)$ is the restriction of a $\bar{\varphi} \in C^2(N)$; see the appendix for the local extensions which are then glued together with a partition of unity) we have shown that $J'\cdot\underline{X} = (\overset{2}{j}{}^*J')\cdot\underline{X} = J\cdot\underline{X}$ since $jX = X$. In the case where $N = E$ a real vector space we can write $J' = (J_1,J_2)$ and $j\underline{X} = (X, \frac{1}{2}[X,X])^{\text{transposed}}$ (these expressions depend on the choice of E) and then $J\cdot\underline{X} = J_1\cdot X + \frac{1}{2}J_2\cdot[X,X]$ (which is independent of the choice of E).

Vector-valued semimartingales have a decomposition into characteristic and martingale components. One should be able to do the same for M-semimartingales on an infinitesimal level. To see how one can achieve this we decompose a complete E-semimartingale $\underline{X} = \begin{pmatrix} X \\ \frac{1}{2}[X,X] \end{pmatrix}$ as $\underline{X} = \underline{X}^c + \underline{\tilde{X}}$ where $\underline{X}^c = \begin{pmatrix} X^c \\ 0 \end{pmatrix}$ and $\underline{\tilde{X}} = \begin{pmatrix} \tilde{X} \\ \frac{1}{2}[X,X] \end{pmatrix}$. If $\Phi: E \to F$, F another real vector space, and $Y = \Phi(X)$ then in the formal transformation $d\underline{Y}_t = \overset{2}{\Phi}(X_t)d\underline{X}_t$ we can read off the resulting relations $d\underline{Y}_t^c = \Phi'(X_t)d\underline{X}_t^c$ and $d\underline{\tilde{Y}}_t = \overset{2}{\Phi}(X_t)d\underline{\tilde{X}}_t$. In other words $d\underline{X}_t^c$ and $d\underline{\tilde{X}}_t$ behave (transform) as first and second order tangent vectors respectively at the point X_t. It stands to reason that there should be a version of the previous theorem for quantities $\int_0^t (J_s|d\underline{X}_s^c)$ and $\int_0^t (J_s|d\underline{\tilde{X}}_s)$. Indeed there is such an existence theorem. For instance we can show that there is a unique Opt-linear map $T^{*1}(M;X) \to \mathrm{Opt}\,\mathcal{M}^c$ denoted by $J \mapsto \int_0^t (J_s|dX_s^c)$ or $J \cdot X^c$ such that $D^1\varphi(X) \mapsto \varphi(X)^c$ for $\varphi \in C^1(M)$. The proof is virtually the same as that given for the theorem; in part (ii) we argue along the same lines to verify that $\Sigma\alpha_\ell D^1\varphi_\ell(X) = 0$ implies $\Sigma\alpha_\ell \cdot \varphi_\ell(X)^c = 0$ using the fact that $\psi(Y)^c = \psi'(Y)\cdot Y$ for an E-semimartingale Y and $\psi \in C^2(E)$. Denoting the projection $T^{*2}(M;X) \overset{i^*}{\to} T^{*1}(M;X)$ we can lift $\cdot X^c$ to a unique Opt-linear map $\cdot\underline{X}^c : T^{*2}(M;X) \to \mathrm{Opt}\mathcal{M}^c$ such that $D^2\varphi(X)\cdot\underline{X}^c = \varphi(X)^c$ for $\varphi \in C^2(M)$. Defining $\cdot\underline{\tilde{X}} = \cdot X - \cdot\underline{X}^c$ gives us the unique Opt-linear map from $T^{*2}(M;X)$ into $\mathrm{Opt}\mathcal{V}^c$ such that $D^2\varphi(X)\cdot\underline{\tilde{X}} = \widetilde{\varphi(X)} - \varphi(X_0)$. Thus in an alternate notation we can write $d\underline{X}_t = d\underline{X}_t^c + d\underline{\tilde{X}}_t$ (which can be interpreted as the equality of two measures in the vectorial case) in the sense that $\int_0^t (J_s|d\underline{X}_s) = \int_0^t (J_s|d\underline{X}_c^c) + \int_0^t (J_s|d\underline{\tilde{X}}_s)$ (i.e. $J\cdot\underline{X} = J\cdot\underline{X}^c + J.\underline{\tilde{X}}$) for all $J \in T^{*2}(M;X)$. We summarize the results obtained so far in this section, in the following theorem.

Theorem. Let X be a continuous M-semimartingale, $T^{*k}(M;X)$ the Opt-module of optional $T^{*k}(M)$-valued processes J such that $J(t,\omega) \in T^{*k}(M,X(t,\omega))$ for $\mathbb{P}$-a.e. ω, $t \in \bar{\mathbb{R}}_+$, k=1,2. There exist unique Opt-linear maps $T^{*2}(M;X) \to \mathrm{Opt}\mathcal{SM}^c$ denoted by $J \mapsto J\cdot\underline{X}$ (or $\int_0^t (J_s|d\underline{X}_s)$), $J \mapsto J.\underline{X}^c$ (or $\int_0^t (J_s|d\underline{X}_s^c)$, a unique Opt-linear map $T^{*2}(M;X) \to \mathrm{Opt}\mathcal{V}^c$, denoted by $J \mapsto J\cdot\underline{\tilde{X}}$ (or $\int_0^t (J_s|d\underline{\tilde{X}}_s)$) for $J \in T^{*2}(M;X)$, and a unique Opt-linear map $T^{*1}(M;X) \to \mathrm{Opt}\mathcal{M}^c$ denoted by $J \mapsto J\cdot X^c$ (or $\int_0^t (J_s|dX_s^c)$), for $J \in T^{*1}(M;X)$, such that for $\varphi \in C^2(M)$:

(i) $D^2\varphi(X)\cdot\underline{X} = \varphi(X) - \varphi(X_0)$

(ii) $D^2\varphi(X)\cdot\underline{X}^c = \varphi(X)^c$

(iii) $D^2\varphi(X)\cdot\underline{\tilde{X}} = \widetilde{\varphi(X)} - \varphi(X_0)$

(iv) $D^1\varphi(X)\cdot X^c = \varphi(X)^c$.

Moreover $\cdot\underline{X} = \cdot\underline{X}^c + \cdot\underline{\tilde{X}}$ ("infinitesimally": $d\underline{X}_t = d\underline{X}_t^c + d\underline{\tilde{X}}_t$), $(J.\underline{X})^c = J\cdot\underline{X}^c$, $(J\cdot\underline{X})^\sim = J\cdot\underline{\tilde{X}}$, and if $j^*: T^{*2}(M;X) \to T^{*1}(M;X)$ denotes the natural projection, then $.\underline{X}^c = (\cdot X^c)\circ j^*$. If $\Phi \in C^2(M,N)$, $Y = \Phi(X)$ and $J \in T^{*2}(N;Y)$, then $\int_0^t (J_s|d\underline{Y}_s) = \int_0^t (\overset{2}{\Phi}{}^*_X J_s|d\underline{X}_s)$ ("infinitesimally": $d((\Phi(X))_t = \overset{2}{\Phi}[dX_t])$; and similarly for $d\underline{X}_t^c$, $d\tilde{\underline{X}}_t$, and dX_t^c. □

As an illustration of these differentials, consider a diffusion on M. By this we mean: $\Omega = C(\bar{R}_+, M)$ (no explosions for simplicity here), $\mathcal{O}$ = Borel σ-algebra, $(\mathbb{P}_x)_{x \in M}$ a family of probability measures on $(\Omega, \mathcal{O})$, $\mathcal{T}_t = \sigma(X_s;\ 0 \le s \le t)$ (where $X_t(\omega) = \omega(t)$) suitably augmented to satisfy the usual hypotheses, and for some strictly elliptic second order differential operator L without term of order zero (the infinitesimal generator):

(i) $\mathbb{P}_x(X_0 = x) = 1$, for each $x \in M$

(ii) for each $\varphi \in C^2(M)$ and $x \in M$, $\varphi(X) - \varphi(X_0) - \int_0^t L\varphi(X_s)ds$ is a continuous local $\mathbb{P}_x$-martingale (in fact a martingale if φ has compact support)

and P_x is the unique probability measure satisfying (i) and (ii). This is the Strook-Varadhan approach. Condition (ii) implies that each φ(X) is a continuous real semimartingale, therefore X is a continuous M-semimartingale.

We can rewrite condition (ii) as $D^2\varphi(X) \cdot \underline{X} - \int_0^t (D^2\varphi(X_s) | L_{X_s})ds \in \mathcal{M}^c$. Now $\int_0^t (D^2\varphi(X_s) | L_{X_s})ds \in \mathcal{V}^c$, therefore by uniqueness $\int_0^t (D^2\varphi(X_s) | L_{X_s})ds = (D^2\varphi(X) \cdot \underline{X})^\sim$ which is $D^2\varphi(X) \cdot \tilde{\underline{X}}$ by the previous theorem. Since $\{D^2\varphi(X) : \varphi \in C^2(M)\}$ generates $T^{*2}(M;X)$ we obtain $\int_0^t (J_s | d\tilde{\underline{X}}_s) = \int_0^t (J_s | L_{X_s})ds$ for all $J \in T^{*2}(M;X)$. Thus it is apt to write $d\tilde{\underline{X}}_t = L_{X_t} dt$. We shall return to this denotation after discussing tangential representations. Note that in the equality $(J\cdot\underline{X})^{\sim} = \int_0^t (J_s | L_{X_s})ds$ both the stochastic integration "." and the characteristic projection "~" depend on $\mathbb{P}_X$, but their composition in this instance evidently does not.

6 APPENDIX

In this appendix we outline some alternate proofs of condition (ii) in the proof of the first theorem of this section. The first proof utilizes the notion of stochastic integration with respect to locally defined semimartingales, which was outlined in the appendix to the section on the localization principle.

Recall that we wish to show that $\sum_{\text{finite}} \alpha_\ell D^2\varphi_\ell(X) = 0$ implies $\Sigma\alpha_\ell\cdot\varphi_\ell(X) = 0$ where $\alpha_\ell \in$ Opt and $\varphi_\ell \in C^2(M)$, X being a continuous M-semimartingale.

<u>Proof 1</u>. It suffices to show $\Sigma\alpha_\ell\cdot\varphi_\ell(X) \underset{A_n}{\sim} 0$ where $A_n = X^{-1}(V_n)$, $(V_n,\Phi_n)_{n\in\mathbb{N}}$ being an atlas on M. Let $Y_n = \Phi_n(X)$ and $\psi_{\ell,n} = \varphi_\ell\circ\Phi_n^{-1}$. Then on A_n:

$$0 = (\overset{2}{\Phi}{}_n^{-1})^*_X\ [\Sigma\alpha_\ell D^2\varphi_\ell(\Phi_n^{-1}(\ Y_n))] = \Sigma\alpha_\ell D^2\psi_{\ell,n}(Y_n)$$

and by Itô's formula: $\psi_{\ell,n}(Y_n) \underset{A_n}{\sim} D^2\psi_{\ell,n}(Y_n)\cdot\underline{Y}_n$. Therefore,

$$\begin{aligned}\Sigma\alpha_\ell\cdot\varphi_\ell(X) &\underset{A_n}{\sim} \Sigma\alpha_\ell\cdot\psi_{\ell,n}(Y_n)\\ &\underset{A_n}{\sim} \Sigma\alpha_\ell\cdot[D^2\psi_{\ell,n}(Y_n)\cdot\underline{Y}_n]\\ &\underset{A_n}{\sim} [\Sigma\alpha_\ell D^2\psi_{\ell,n}(Y_n)]\cdot\underline{Y}_n\\ &\underset{A_n}{\sim} 0.\end{aligned}$$ □

<u>Proof 2.</u> Embed $M \hookrightarrow E$, a 2d-dimensional real vector space (where $\dim M = d$), and let (V,Φ) be a member of a sequence of charts on E such that $\Phi(V) = U\times F$, where F is a d-dimensional real vector space and U is an open set in R^d, and moreover $\Phi(M\cap V) = U\times\{0\}$. Express $V = \bigcup_n V_n$ with V_n open and $\bar{V}_n \subset V$ for all $n \in N$. It suffices to show that $\Sigma\alpha_\ell\cdot\varphi_\ell(X) \underset{A_n}{\sim} 0$ for $A_n := X^{-1}(V_n) = X^{-1}(V_n\cap M)$ (disregard the trivial cases when A_n is empty). Fix n and let $\beta \in C^2(E)$ with $\operatorname{supp}\beta \subset V$ and $\beta = 1$ on a neighbourhood of $\bar{V}_n$.

We define a map $\theta:\varphi \mapsto \bar{\varphi}$, $\theta:C^2_{(0)}(M;x) \to C^2_{(0)}(E;x)$ for $x \in V_n$ as follows. Since E is a product over V we extend φ to be constant on the fibres and multiply by β. More precisely if $\pi:U\times F \to F$ is the projection, then $\bar{\varphi} = \beta.[\varphi\circ\Phi^{-1}\circ\pi\circ\Phi]$. Clearly $\theta[C^2_{(2)}(M:x)] \subset C^2_{(2)}(E;x)$ so we have an induced linear map $\bar{\theta}_x:T^{*2}(M,x) \to T^{*2}(E,x)$ such that $\bar{\theta}_x D^2\varphi(x) = D^2\bar{\varphi}(x)$ for each $x \in V_n\cap M$ and $\varphi \in C^2(M)$.

We are given $\Sigma\alpha_\ell D^2\varphi_\ell(X) = 0$, so that on A_n:

$$0 = \bar{\theta}_X[\Sigma\alpha_\ell D^2\varphi_\ell(X)] = \Sigma\alpha_\ell D^2\bar{\varphi}_\ell(X) .$$

Therefore

$0 \underset{A_n}{\sim} \Sigma\alpha_\ell D^2\bar{\varphi}_\ell(X).\underline{X}$ (integration in E)

$\underset{A_n}{\sim} \Sigma\alpha_\ell\cdot\bar{\varphi}_\ell(X)$ (Itô's formula)

$\underset{A_n}{\sim} \Sigma\alpha_\ell\cdot\varphi_\ell(X)$ (by an equivalence theorem; $\bar{\varphi} = \varphi$ on $V_n\cap M$, $X(A_n)\subset V_n\cap M$). □

<u>Proof 3.</u> In this proof we admit the existence of a tubular neighbourhood G of M, G being non-uniform in general, when M is embedded into E a finite dimensional real vector space. That is, G is simultaneously open in E, a neighbourhood of M, and a C^2 fiber bundle over M with projection, say $\pi:G \to M$. Fix a $\beta \in C^2(E)$ with $\mathrm{supp}\beta \subset G$ and $\beta = 1$ on a subtubular neighbourhood of M. Given $\varphi \in C^2(M)$ extend it to $\bar{\varphi} := \beta.\tilde{\varphi}$ where $\tilde{\varphi}$ is constant along the fibers of G. Then we have $\pi_x^* D^2\varphi(x) = D^2\bar{\varphi}(x)$ for all $x \in M$. Thus $\Sigma\alpha_\ell D^2\varphi_\ell(X) = 0$ implies $\Sigma\alpha_\ell D^2\bar{\varphi}_\ell(X) = 0$ and by Itô's formula and two equivalence theorems:

$0 = \Sigma\alpha_\ell D^2\bar{\varphi}_\ell(X)\cdot\underline{X}$ (integration in E)

$= \Sigma\alpha_\ell\cdot\bar{\varphi}_\ell(X)$

$= \Sigma\alpha_\ell\cdot\varphi_\ell(X)$

□

CHAPTER 9

THE TANGENT SPACE TO A SEMIMARTINGALE AND TANGENTIAL REPRESENTATIONS

We have seen that the differential $d\underset{\sim}{X}_t$ of a continuous M-semimartingale may be viewed informally as an element of $T^2(M,X_t)$. It may happen that $d\underset{\sim}{X}_t$ actually lies in a smaller subspace. For instance if X were of finite variation then $d\underset{\sim}{X}_t$ would lie in $T^1(M,X_t)$ (at least almost everywhere along X_t, with respect to arc length measure). One of the purposes of this section is to make this notion of minimal tangent subspace more precise. In order that the theory be applicable simultaneously for $d\underline{X}$, $d\underline{X}^c$, $d\underline{\tilde{X}}$, an abstract presentation will be given which should also clarify the essential ideas. In the second part of this section the notion of a tangential representation is discussed; it provides the basis of a global definition of a stochastic differential equation on a manifold.

We begin with some definitions and terminology. Let $\mathbb{V} \overset{\pi}{\to} B$ be a Borel vector bundle; that is, we relax the condition of continuity of the transition coordinate maps and the projection π, to only Borel measurability. Denote by $\mathbb{V}^* \overset{\pi}{\to} B$ the dual bundle and let $X:\bar{\mathbb{R}}_+\times\Omega \to B$ be an optional process. We define $\mathbb{V}^*(X)$ to be the Opt-module of optional processes $J:\bar{\mathbb{R}}_+\times\Omega \to \mathbb{V}^*$ such that $\pi J(t,\omega) = X(t,\omega)$ for each t and $\mathbb{P}$-a.e. ω.

The expression "du $\in \mathbb{V}$ is an infinitesimal element of a continuous semimartingale along X" (briefly, "du $\in \mathbb{V}$ along X") means that there is given an Opt-linear map $u:\mathbb{V}^*(X) \to \mathrm{Opt}\mathcal{SM}_0^c$, written $J \mapsto J\cdot u$. As examples, we have with $B = M$, $\mathbb{V} = T^2(M)$, and X an M-semimartingale, the choices: $du = d\underline{X}$, $d\underline{X}^c$, or $d\underline{\tilde{X}}$. Note that $V^*(X) = T^{*2}(M;X)$ in this case.

An optional *field of subspaces of* $\mathbb{V}$ *over* X is an optional process $F:\bar{\mathbb{R}}_+\times\Omega \to$ Grassmannian of V such that $F(t,\omega) \subset F_{\mathbb{V}}(X(t,\omega)) := \pi^{-1}X(t,\omega)$, the fiber over $X(t,\omega)$. Alternately it can be characterized by the existence of optional processes with values in $\mathbb{V}$, and over X, which span $F(t,\omega)$. We also define for such a field F, the annihilator $F^{\perp}$, the optional field of subspaces of $\mathbb{V}^*$ over X containing those $J \in \mathbb{V}^*(X)$ such that $(J|v) = 0$ for all $v \in F$; we write $J \perp F$ in this case.

An optional set $A \subset \bar{\mathbb{R}}_+ \times \Omega$ is called du-*negligible* if $J \cdot u = 0$ for all $J \in \mathbb{V}^*(X)$ supported by A. In general an arbitrary subset $A \subset \bar{\mathbb{R}}_+ \times \Omega$ is called du-negligible if there exists an optional du-negligible set containing A.

If F is an optional field of subspaces of $\mathbb{V}$ over X and $du \in \mathbb{V}$ we say that "du takes its values in F" or $du \in F$ if $J \cdot u = 0$ du-a.e. whenever $J \perp F$. The requirement $J \cdot u = 0$ is only taken off of a du-negligible set since even for a curve γ of finite variation, $\dot{\gamma}$ is only specified a.e. with respect to arclength along γ. We can now state the theorem concerning the minimal optional field of subspaces containing du. When $du = dX$, etc., it is called the tangent space to X, etc.

Theorem. If $du \in \mathbb{V}$ along X, then there exists a smallest (up to du-negligibility) optional field $\tau(u)$ of subspaces of $\mathbb{V}$ along X, containing du; i.e.:

(1) $J \perp \tau(u)$ implies $J \cdot u = 0$ du-a.e.

(2) If F is an optional field of subspaces of $\mathbb{V}$ along X and $J \perp F$ implies $J \cdot u = 0$ du-a.e., then $\tau(u) \subset F$ du-a.e..

Remark. The proof uses the fact that any L^0-valued measure (or Banach valued measure) has an equivalent positive (real) measure.

Suppose $\mathbb{V} \overset{\pi_B}{\to} B$ and $\mathbb{W} \overset{\pi_C}{\to} C$ are two Borel vector bundles and $\mathbb{L}:\mathbb{V} \to \mathbb{W}$ is a Borel vector bundle map. Then if $du \in \mathbb{V}$ along X, in B, we can define an infinitesimal element $\mathbb{L}du \in \mathbb{W}$ along $Y = \pi_C \circ \mathbb{L}$, also written $d(\mathbb{L}.u)$, by $J\cdot(\mathbb{L}\cdot u) = (\mathbb{L}^*_X J)\cdot u$ since for $\alpha \in \mathrm{Opt}$: $(\alpha J)\cdot(\mathbb{L}\cdot u) = (\mathbb{L}^*[\alpha J])\cdot u = (\alpha\mathbb{L}^*[J])\cdot u = \alpha\cdot[(\mathbb{L}^*J)\cdot u] = \alpha\cdot[J\cdot(\mathbb{L}\cdot u)]$. Note that $\mathbb{L}^*_X J$ is optional. More generally, we can allow $\mathbb{L}$ to be stochastic by considering an optional process $\mathbb{L}:\bar{\mathbb{R}}_+ \times \Omega \to \mathcal{L}(\mathbb{V},\mathbb{W})$, the vector bundle over $B\times C$ whose fiber over (b,c), $F_{\mathcal{L}(\mathbb{V},\mathbb{W})}(b,c)$, is $\mathcal{L}(F_{\mathbb{V}}(b), F_{\mathbb{W}}(x))$; the definition of $\mathbb{L}\cdot u$ remains the same: $J\cdot(\mathbb{L}\cdot u) = (\mathbb{L}^*J)\cdot u$. If $\mathbb{L}:\mathbb{V} \to \mathbb{W}$ then the action of $\mathbb{L}$ and $\mathbb{L}(t,\omega) := \mathbb{L}(X(t,\omega))$ coincide. The case $\mathbb{L} = \overset{2}{\Phi}$ (equivalently $\overset{2}{\Phi}(X)$) is noteworthy; see the discussion after the remark, p. 145 Note that $Y = \pi_C \circ \mathbb{L}$ is automatically optional. If $\mathbb{L}':\mathbb{W} \to \mathbb{U}$ is another vector bundle map then it is easy to check that $\mathbb{L}'(\mathbb{L}du) = (\mathbb{L}' \circ \mathbb{L})du$.

The determination of $\tau(\mathbb{L}du)$ is given in the next theorem which we state without proof. The remark following the previous theorem applies here as well.

<u>Theorem</u>. If $du \in \mathbb{V}$ along X and $\mathbb{L}:\bar{\mathbb{R}}_+ \times \Omega \to \mathcal{L}(\mathbb{V},\mathbb{W})$ is an optional process then $\tau(\mathbb{L}du) = \mathbb{L}\tau(u)$, $\mathbb{L}du$-a.e..

<u>Corollary</u>. $\mathbb{L}du = 0$ iff $\tau(u) \subset \ker\mathbb{L}$, du-a.e. (which is stronger than $\mathbb{L}du$-a.e.).

We now turn to the topic of tangential representations. Let $du \in \mathbb{V}$ along X. Given m continuous real semimartingales $Z^{(k)}$ and m optional processes $g_{(k)} \in \mathbb{V}(X)$ we say that we have a tangential representation of du, written $du = \sum_{k=1}^{m} g_{(k)} dZ^{(k)}$ or $u = \sum_k g_{(k)} \cdot Z^{(k)}$, if $J \cdot u = \sum_k (J|g_{(k)}) \cdot Z^{(k)}$, for all $J \in \mathbb{V}^*(X)$. This can also be written as an equality of measures: $d(J \cdot u) = \sum_k (J|g_{(k)}) dZ^{(k)}$. Such representations always exist.

As an example, let X be a continuous E-semimartingale with $(e_k)_{k=1}^{d}$ a basis of E. Then Itô's formula, written in the form: $d\underline{X} = \sum_{k=1}^{d} \begin{pmatrix} e_k \\ 0 \end{pmatrix} dX^{(k)} + \sum_{i,j=1}^{d} \begin{pmatrix} 0 \\ e_i \odot e_j \end{pmatrix} d[X^{(i)}, X^{(j)}]/2$ supplies us with a tangential representation of $d\underline{X}$, where $X = \sum_k X^{(k)} e_k$.

In general, if $du \in \mathbb{V}$ along X, we can take $(g_{(k)})_{k=1}^{m}$ an optional basis of $\mathbb{V}(X)$, $((g_{(k)}(t,\omega))_{k=1}^{m}$ is a basis of $F_{\mathbb{V}}(X(t,\omega))$ where m is the dimension of the fibers of $\mathbb{V}$, and set $(J^{(k)})_{k=1}^{m}$ to be the dual basis. Then if $J \in \mathbb{V}^*(X)$, we can write $J = \sum_{k=1}^{n} (J|g_{(k)}) J^{(k)}$, and so $J \cdot u = \sum_k (J|g_{(k)}) \cdot (J^{(k)} \cdot u)$. Thus we have a tangential representation $du = \sum_{k=1}^{m} g_{(k)} dZ^{(k)}$ with $Z^{(k)} := J^{(k)} \cdot u$; actually only $Z^{(k)} \in \mathrm{Opt}\mathcal{SM}_0^c$ is guaranteed, so expressing

$Z^{(k)} = \alpha_{(k)}\bar{Z}^{(k)}$ with $\alpha_{(k)} \in$ BOpt and $\bar{Z}^{(k)} \in \mathcal{SM}_0^c$ we can replace $Z^{(k)}$ with $\bar{Z}^{(k)}$ and $g_{(k)}$ with $\bar{g}_{(k)} = \alpha_{(k)} g_{(k)}$: $du = \sum_{k=1}^{m} \bar{g}_{(k)} d\bar{Z}^{(k)}$.

Given a tangential representation $du = \sum_k g_{(k)} dZ^{(k)}$ it is clear that du takes its values in the linear span of $g_{(1)},\ldots,g_{(m)}$. Since $du \in \tau(u)$ the following theorem should not be surprising.

Theorem. If $du \in \mathbb{V}$ along X and has the tangential representation $du = \sum_{k=1}^{m} g_{(k)} dZ^{(k)}$ then $\tau(u) \subset$ linear span $[g_{(1)},\ldots,g_{(n)}]$ du-a.e.. It is always possible to arrange to have a tangential representation $du = \sum_{k=1}^{m} g_{(k)} dZ^{(k)}$ with $\tau(u) =$ linear span $[g_{(1)},\ldots,g_{(m)}]$.

As an example, consider as in the previous section, a diffusion X_t with infinitesimal generator L. Then $d\underset{\sim}{X}$ has the tangential representation $d\underset{\sim}{X} = L_X dt$ with m=1, $g=L_X$, and $Z : (t,\omega) \mapsto t$. Evidently, $\tau(d\underset{\sim}{X})$ is one dimensional (unless L is very degenerate) with $\tau(d\underset{\sim}{X})(t,\omega) = \mathbb{R}L_{X(t,\omega)}$.

In closing this section, if $\mathbb{L}:\mathbb{V} \to \mathbb{W}$ or $\mathbb{L}:\bar{\mathbb{R}}_+\times\Omega \to \mathcal{L}(\mathbb{V},\mathbb{W})$ is optional, and $du = \sum_k g_{(k)} dZ^{(k)}$ then $\mathbb{L}du = \sum_k \mathbb{L}_{g_{(k)}} dZ^{(k)}$ is straightforward to derive. The cases $\mathbb{L}(t,\omega) = \mathbb{L}(X(t,\omega))$ and $\mathbb{L}(t,\omega) = \overset{2}{\Phi}(X(t,\omega))$, $\Phi \in C^2(M,N)$ are extremely important and will be used often.

CHAPTER 10

STOCHASTIC DIFFERENTIAL EQUATIONS

We begin with the vector-valued case. Let E be a finite dimensional real vector space. The ingredients of a stochastic differential equation, SDE, are m continuous real-valued semimartingales Z^k and m continuous E-valued vector fields H_k (which we take to be deterministic for simplicity) defined on E or more generally an open subset U of E. The problem is to find a continuous E-semimartingale (respectively U-semimartingale) X which satisfies the equation:

$$\text{(SDE)}: \quad dX = \sum_{k=1}^{m} H_k(X)dZ^k \quad \text{or} \quad X - X_0 = \sum_{k=1}^{m} H_k(X)\cdot Z^k .$$

The latter integrated version may also be written as $X \sim \sum_{k=1}^{m} H_k(X)\cdot Z^k$, with equivalence here on all of $\bar{\mathbb{R}}_+ \times \Omega$. This formulation is useful when considering the more general situation in which the semimartingales are only locally defined; this is in keeping with the notion and notation of stochastic integration for them (see the appendix to the section on the localization principle).

Usually, an initial value $X_0 = a \in \mathcal{F}_0$ is prescribed in advance. As such, if the H_k's are globally Lipschitz, then SDE can be solved by Picard iteration (the usual method of successive approximations) yielding a unique solution $X \in \mathcal{SM}^c$, with $X_0 = a$ on all of $\bar{\mathbb{R}}_+ \times \Omega$. If the H_k's are only locally Lipschitz then there exists a unique maximal solution X on some stochastic interval $[0,\zeta[$ where ζ, the "death time" or "explosion time", is a predictable strictly positive stopping time:

$$[0,\zeta(\omega)[\;=\; \begin{cases} [0,\zeta(\omega)[, & \text{if } \zeta(\omega) \leq +\infty \\ [0,\zeta(\omega)[\;=\; \bar{\mathbb{R}}_+ \times \Omega, & \text{if } \zeta(\omega) = \overline{+\infty} \end{cases}$$

(Strictly speaking, we have not discussed stochastic integration on such a set, as yet; this will be commented on, in a remark, further on in this section.)

It turns out that in the case $\zeta(\omega) = \overline{+\infty}$ then $X(\omega)$ is continuous on $\bar{\mathbb{R}}_+$; in the case $\zeta(\omega) \leq +\infty$ then $X_t(\omega) \to \infty$ as $t \to \zeta(\omega)$ $\mathbb{P}$-a.e.. This dichotomy is illustrated by the following example for $E = \mathbb{R}^1$ in which we contrast the behaviour of the solution X of a SDE with $Z \in \mathcal{V}^c$ versus $Z \in \mathcal{M}^c$. Let $Z = (t)$ denote the process $(t,\omega) \mapsto t \wedge 1$ and $H(x) = x^2$, $x \in E = \mathbb{R}^1$. Then $X = 1 + H(X) \cdot (t)$ has the unique maximal solution, $X_t = 1/(1-t)$ on $[0,1[$ i.e. $\zeta \equiv 1$. On the other hand if $Z = M \in \mathcal{M}^c$ and $a \in \mathcal{T}_0$, then for the unique maximal solution X of $X = a+H(X)\cdot M$, $\zeta \equiv \overline{+\infty}$. This result is due to Lenglart who pointed out that since any continuous real martingale is a random time change of a Brownian motion, $|X_t|\to+\infty$ is ruled out.

The local existence of a solution of SDE in the locally Lipschitz case is reduced to that of the globally Lipschitz case with the aid of the localization principle. The proof will be outlined later, for the more general case of a SDE on a manifold.

Turning our attention now to defining a SDE on a manifold, we have seen that it is not dX but rather $d\underline{X} = \begin{pmatrix} dX \\ \frac{1}{2}d[X,X] \end{pmatrix}$ which behaves as a geometric object. It is thus natural to recast SDE as an uncoupled system for $\underline{X}$. If $X = X_0 + \sum_{k=1}^{m} H_k(X)\cdot Z^k$ then $\frac{1}{2}[X,X] = \frac{1}{2}X_0 \odot X_0 + \frac{1}{2} \sum_{1\le i,j\le m} H_i(X)\odot H_j(X)\cdot[Z^i,Z^j]$. Note that if we subject E to a C^2 diffeomorphism (i.e. change of coordinates) then the SDE would then contain terms of the form $[Z^i,Z^j]$, even if not so initially, as results from Itô's formula. Thus it is more natural to assume, without any loss or gain of analytic generality, that they do appear initially:

$$\text{(SDE')} \quad X = X_0 + \sum_{k=1}^{m} H_k(X)\cdot Z^k + \frac{1}{2} \sum_{1\le i,j\le m} H_{ij}(X)\cdot[Z^i,Z^j] \quad (H_{ij}=H_{ji}).$$

Then for $\underline{X}$ we have:

$$(\underline{SDE}): \quad \underline{X} = \underline{X}_0 + \sum_{k=1}^{m} \overset{(1)}{H_k}(X)\cdot Z^k + \frac{1}{2} \sum_{1\leq i,j\leq m} \overset{(2)}{H_{ij}}(X)\cdot[Z^i,Z^j]$$

where $\underline{X}_0 = \begin{pmatrix} X_0 \\ X_0 \odot X_0 \end{pmatrix}$, $\overset{(1)}{H_k} = \begin{pmatrix} H_k \\ 0 \end{pmatrix}$, and $\overset{(2)}{H_{ij}} = \begin{pmatrix} H_{ij} \\ H_i \odot H_j \end{pmatrix}$.

Two remarks are in order at this point. Firstly, the system $\underline{SDE}$ is extremely uncoupled; after solving the equation for the first component X, the equation for the second component is automatically satisfied by $\frac{1}{2}[X,X]$. Secondly, the vectors $\overset{(1)}{H_k} \in T^1(E,\cdot)$ and the vectors $\overset{(2)}{H_{ij}} \in T^2(E,\cdot)$ are not arbitrary; $\overset{(2)}{H_{ij}} = \overset{(2)}{H_{ji}}$ and if $pr:T^2 \to T^2/T^1 = T^1 \odot T^1$ then $pr\,\overset{(2)}{H_{ij}} = \overset{(1)}{H_i} \odot \overset{(1)}{H_j}$. This leads us to the following definition.

Definition. Let M be a $C^{2,1}$ manifold, i.e. the change of coordinate maps are $C^{2,1}$ ($C^{n,1}$ being the C^n maps whose n^{th} derivatives are locally Lipschitz). Let $(Z^k)_{k=1}^m$ be m continuous real semimartingales, $(H_k)_{k=1}^m$ and $(H_{ij})_{1\leq i,j\leq m}$ $C^{0,1}$ sections of $T^1(M)$ and $T^2(M)$ respectively, such that $H_{ij} = H_{ji}$ and $prH_{ij} = H_i \odot H_j$ where $pr:T^2(M) \to T^2(M)/T^1(M) = T^1(M) \odot T^1(M)$. The corresponding stochastic differential equation $\underline{SDE}$ (or simply SDE if M is not an open subset of a Euclidean space) is:

$$(\underline{SDE}) \quad d\underline{X} = \sum_{k=1}^{m} H_k(X)dZ^k + \frac{1}{2} \sum_{1\leq i,j\leq m} H_{ij}(X)d[Z^i,Z^j]$$

in the sense of tangential representations, i.e. X is a solution of SDE if X is a continuous M-semimartingale and for all $J \in T^{*2}(M;X)$:

$$J.\underline{X} = \sum_{k=1}^{m} (J|H_k(X)) \cdot Z^k + \frac{1}{2} \sum_{1 \leq i,j \leq m} (J|H_{ij}(X)) \cdot [Z^i, Z^j].$$

It suffices that the identity above be valid for J of the form $J = D^2\varphi(X)$ for arbitrary $\varphi \in C^2(M)$, in which case it reads:

$$\varphi(X) - \varphi(X_0) = \sum_{k=1}^{m} (D^1\varphi(X)|H_k(X)) \cdot Z^k$$

$$+ \frac{1}{2} \sum_{1 \leq i,j \leq m} (D^2\varphi(X)|H_{ij}(X)) \cdot [Z^i, Z^j] .$$

One can also prescribe an initial condition $X_0 = a \in \mathcal{T}_0$.

Remark. The $C^{2,1}$ hypotheses in the definition can be replaced *everywhere* by simply C^2, but if we wish to consider *locally Lipschitz* vector fields, which is defined via charts, then the term locally Lipschitz will have a chart-independent meaning only if M is $C^{2,1}$. We included this extra regularity condition right at the outset since it is sufficient (though not necessary) for the establishment of an existence and uniqueness theorem for solutions, but continuity alone is not sufficient.

In the linear case M=E, it is clear that every $X \in \mathcal{SM}^c$ is the solution of at least one SDE stemming from the identity $d\underline{X} = d\underline{X}$ written out in coordinates

$$d\underline{X} = \sum_{k=1}^{d} e_k dZ^k + \frac{1}{2} \sum_{1\le i,j\le d} e_i \odot e_j d[Z^i, Z^j]$$

where $d = \dim E$, $\{e_k\}_{k=1}^{d}$ is a basis of E, and Z^k is the kth coordinate of X with respect to this basis. It is not quite as evident that in general every M-semimartingale is a solution of at least one SDE. Since we will need this result in the next section we prove it here.

Proposition. Let M be $C^{2,1}$ d-dimensional manifold and X a continuous M-semimartingale. Then X satisfies at least one SDE.

Proof. From our work on transformations of tangential representations, we may assume M is embedded as a closed submanifold of E, a 2d-dimensional real vector space. Consider two vector bundles, one being trivial: $M\times E$, the other being $T^1(M)$. Denote by $p: M\times E \to T^1(M)$ the vector bundle projection: $p(x)$ for $x \in M$ is the orthogonal projection of $E = T^1(E,x)$ onto $T^1(M,x)$; p is then a $C^{1,1}$ map. We shall establish in a moment the existence of a $C^{0,1}$ vector bundle map $\bar{p}: M\times[E\oplus(E\odot E)] \to T^2(M)$ having the following two properties:

(A) $\bar{p}$ coincides with p on $M\times E$. Thus $\bar{p}$ induces a map: $M\times(E\odot E) \to T^2(M)/T^1(M) = T^1(M)\odot T^1(M)$; its action coincides with $p\odot p$.

(B) $\bar{p}$ is the identity on $T^2(M) \subset M\times[E\oplus(E\odot E)]$.

Granting the existence of such a map, p(X) may play the role of the maps $\mathbb{L}$, previously studied on vector bundles, acting on the infinitesimal processes du (see the section on tangential representations). Let $\{e_k\}_{k=1}^{2d}$ be a basis of E and $(Z^k)_{k=1}^{2d}$ the coordinates of X with respect to this basis. We have, reasoning on E:

$$d\underline{X} = \sum_{k=1}^{2d} e_k dZ^k + \frac{1}{2} \sum_{i \le i, j \le 2d} e_i \odot e_j \, d[Z^i, Z^j].$$

Since $d\underline{X}$ takes its values in $T^2(M)$, on which $\bar{p}$ is the identity $d\underline{X} = p(X)d\underline{X}$. By property (B) we can develop this equality as:

$$\text{(\underline{SDE})} \qquad d\underline{X} = \sum_{k=1}^{2d} p(X) e_k dZ^k + \frac{1}{2} \sum_{1 \le i, j \le 2d} p(X)(e_i \odot e_j) d[Z^i, Z^j].$$

Indeed, by property (A) the image of $p(x)(e_i \odot e_j)$ in $T^1(M) \odot T^1(M)$ is $p(x) \circledcirc p(x)(e_i \odot e_j) = p(x)e_i \odot p(x)e_j$ so that we do have a bona fide $\underline{\text{SDE}}$ with the Z^k's as above, $H_k(x) = p(x)e_k$, and $H_{ij}(x) = p(x)(e_i \odot e_j)$.

It only remains to establish the existence of such a map p. Define a vector bundle map $\bar{\mathbb{L}}: M \times [E \oplus (E \odot E)] \to T^2(M)$ by $\bar{\mathbb{L}}(x)(\xi, \Delta) = p(x)\xi + \theta(x)[p(x) \circledcirc p(x)(\Delta)]$, for $x \in M$ and $(\xi, \Delta) \in E \oplus (E \odot E)$, where θ is a $C^{1,1}$ lifting of $T^1(M) \odot T^1(M) \to T^2(M)$. Obviously $\bar{\mathbb{L}}$ coincides with p on $M \times E$ and with $p \circledcirc p$ as a map: $(M \times E) \odot (M \times E) \to T^2(M)/T^1(M) = T^1(M) \odot T^1(M)$. Restricting $\bar{\mathbb{L}}$ to $T^2(M)$ yields a map $\mathbb{L}: T^2(M) \to T^2(M)$ which is the identity on $T^1(M)$. In particular it induces a map

$\tilde{\mathbb{L}}:T^2(M)/T^1(M) \to T^2(M)/T^1(M)$ which is also the identity on $T^1(M)$ (being equivalent to $p \circledcirc p$). Therefore $\mathbb{L}|_{T^1(M)}$ and $\tilde{\mathbb{L}}$ are invertible (on each fiber) which implies that $\mathbb{L}$ itself is invertible (on each fiber) with $\mathbb{L}^{-1}:T^2(M) \to T^2(M)$ being $C^{1,1}$ and also the identity on the subspace $T^1(M)$ and factor space $T^2(M)/T^1(M)$. If we set $\bar{p} = \mathbb{L}^{-1} \circ \bar{\mathbb{L}}$, then $\bar{p}$ is $C^{1,1}$ and satisfies properties (A) and (B). □

Remark. The locally Lipschitz feature plays no essential role; it is merely carried along through the construction and so may be omitted throughout.

We now turn to the question of existence of solutions to a SDE on M. The route we shall take is as follows. Firstly we shall embed $M \hookrightarrow E$, a Euclidean space, and extend the SDE to one on E. Next we shall establish a local existence result on M. Finally we shall indicate why the solution in E stays in M.

Concerning the first step, we might as well consider the general case $M \hookrightarrow N$, both C^2 (or $C^{2,1}$) manifolds with a SDE defined on M. We first extend the H_k's to C^0 (respectively $C^{0,1}$) vector fields $\bar{H}_k$ on N (the extension is easy locally in a chart, wherein N is a product including M as a factor; then use a partition of unity). We can then form $\bar{H}_i \odot \bar{H}_j$ which lifts to an element $\theta(\bar{H}_i \odot \bar{H}_j)$ of $T^2(N)$ via a

C^1 (respectively $C^{1,1}$) lifting $\theta: T^1(N) \odot T^1(N) = T^2(N)/T^1(N) \to T^2(N)$. Note that θ carries $T^1(M) \odot T^1(M)$ into $T^2(M)$. We can then define $\bar{H}_{ij} = \theta(\bar{H}_i \odot \bar{H}_j) + \overline{(H_{ij} - \theta(H_i \odot H_j))}$ where the second summand is any C^0 (respectively $C^{0,1}$) extension of H_{ij} - $\theta(H_i \odot H_j) \in T^1(M)$ to $T^1(N)$. Clearly $\bar{H}_{ij}|_M = \bar{H}_{ij}$, $\bar{H}_{ij} = \bar{H}_{ji}$, and $pr\bar{H}_{ij} = \bar{H}_i \odot \bar{H}_j$ where $pr: T^2(N) \to T^2(N)/T^1(N) = T^1(N) \odot T^1(N)$ since $pr \circ \theta = id$. The $\bar{H}_k$'s, $\bar{H}_{ij}$'s, and Z^k's (from SDE) give us a $\overline{SDE}$ on N and it is not hard to see that a solution of $\overline{SDE}$ with values in M is precisely a solution of SDE on M.

Concerning the second step, we have the following proposition, but first an important remark.

Remark. In order to prove certain results, for instance those of uniqueness, one must work on sets more general than open subsets of $\bar{\mathbb{R}}_+ \times \Omega$; specifically $[S,T]$ with $X_S \in \mathcal{T}_S$ specified. In fact one must work on even more general sets in order to obtain some of the results stated in this section without proof: sets of the form $[S,T| \cap A$ where A is an open subset of $\bar{\mathbb{R}}_+ \times \Omega$, and $[S,T|$ denotes a set of the form $\bigcup_{\omega \in \Omega} [S(\omega), T(\omega)| \times \{\omega\}$ where $T(\omega)|$ is sometimes $T(\omega)[$, sometimes $T(\omega)]$ depending on $\omega \in \Omega$. Here S is a stopping time but T only a time, not necessarily measurable. As such, one must extend the notions and theorems of semimartingales, equivalence, stochastic integration, SDE, etc. to this setting. The details are not deeply difficult but tedious and so will not be carried out here. However one should be aware that this machinery exists and is needed. This setting will be illustrated in the next two propositions.

Proposition. Let S be a stopping time and $a \in \mathcal{T}_S$ with values in M, a $C^{2,1}$ manifold, on which a locally Lipschitz SDE is defined. Then there exists a stopping time $T \geq S$, with $T > S$ on $\{S<+\infty\}$, and a process X on $[S,T]$, the restriction of a global semimartingale (not necessarily continuous on $[0,S]$) which is a solution of SDE on $[S,T]$, and such that $X_S = a$.

Proof. Let $(V_n,\Phi_n)_{n\in N}$ be an atlas on M, with V_n relatively compact, and $(V'_m,\Phi_m)_{m\in N}$ another atlas subordinate to $(V_n,\Phi_n)_{n\in N}$. Fix some n, and for ease of notation assume $\bar{V}'_n \subset V_n$ with common chart Φ_n which transports V_n, V'_n into U_n, U'_n respectively; the latter being relatively compact, open subsets of a vector space E. Also transport the fields H_k, H_{ij} of SDE on V_n via $\overset{2}{\Phi}_n$, yielding a $(\text{SDE})_n$ on U_n. Replace each $\overset{2}{\Phi}_n(H_k)$ on U_n by an L_k which is globally Lipschitz on E and which restricts to $\overset{2}{\Phi}_n(H_k)$ on $\bar{U}'_n$.

Defining $\Omega'_n = \{a \in V'_n\}$ we can then find a solution $Y^{(n)}$ of the SDE on E associated with the L_k's, with the initial condition

$$Y_S^{(n)} = \begin{cases} a & \text{on } \Omega'_n \\ c\in U'_n & \text{on } (\Omega\setminus\Omega'_n) \quad \text{(any constant value in } U'_n \text{ will do).} \end{cases}$$

As has already been pointed out, for a SDE in a vector space E, we only have to solve the part in E; the part in $E \odot E$ is then a consequence. Therefore $Y^{(n)}$ is a solution of $(SDE)_n$ in $(\bar{\mathbb{R}}_+ \times \Omega'_n) \times [S, T'_n]$ with initial value a at time S in Ω'_n, where T'_n is the first exit time from $\bar{U}'_n$. (Note that $(\bar{\mathbb{R}}_+ \times \Omega'_n) \cap [S, T_n] = [S, T''_n|$ where

$$T''_n = \begin{cases} T' \text{ on } \Omega'_n, & \text{in which case } T''_n| = T''_n] \\ S \text{ on } (\Omega \setminus \Omega'_n), & \text{in which case } T''_n| = T''_n[\end{cases}$$

is just a time.)

Transporting back to M we set $X^{(n)} = \overset{2}{\Phi}_n(Y^{(n)})$ (here $Y^{(n)}$ is stopped at time T'_n) we obtain a V'_n-semimartingale satisfying SDE on $[S, T'_n] \cap (\bar{\mathbb{R}}_+ \times \Omega'_n)$ and such that $X^{(n)}_S = a$ on Ω_n. Finally, set $\Omega_0 = \Omega'_0$, $\Omega_1 = \Omega'_1 \setminus \Omega_0, \ldots, \Omega_n = \Omega'_n \setminus \Omega_{n-1}, \ldots;$ and set $T = T'_n$ on Ω_n. Since $[S,T] = \biguplus_{n \in \mathbb{N}} [S, T_n] \cap (\bar{\mathbb{R}}_+ \times \Omega_n)$, a stationary union of semimartingale sets, the localization principle (or the lemma preceding it) yields the existence of a semimartingale X which coincides with $X^{(n)}$ on $[S, T_n] \cap (\bar{\mathbb{R}}_+ \times \Omega_n)$. Then X is a solution of SDE on [S,T] satisfying $X_S = a$. Evidently $T > S$ on $\{S < +\infty\}$. □

(This proposition holds of course for M=E, in which case the proof is slightly simpler, it being unencumbered by the second order structure and the Φ's.)

Concerning the third step, we prove the following proposition.

Proposition. Let M be a closed $C^{2,1}$ submanifold of E, a finite dimensional real vector space. Let SDE be defined on E and tangent to M along M ($H_k(x) \in T^1(M,x)$ for $x \in M$, etc.). Let X be the maximal solution of SDE in E with $a \in \mathcal{T}_0$ its initial value and ζ the corresponding death time. If $a \in M$ then $X \in M$ on all of $[0,\zeta[$.

Proof. Let ζ_M be the first exit time from M. (ζ_M is $\bar{\mathbb{R}}_+ \cup \{\overline{+\infty}\}$-valued) so that $\zeta_M \leq \zeta$. Then X is a solution of SDE on M on $[0,\zeta_M|$ where $\zeta_M| = \zeta_M]$ precisely on $\{\zeta_M < \zeta\}$, in which case $\zeta_M < +\infty$ (for otherwise $\zeta_M \geq +\infty$, $\zeta = \overline{+\infty}$, and $X(\omega)$ is continuous on $[0,+\infty]$ while belonging to closed M in $[0,+\infty[$ hence on $[0,+\infty]$ which implies $\zeta_M = \overline{+\infty}$); $\zeta_M| = \zeta_M[$ precisely on $\{\zeta_M = \zeta\}$. By the local existence theorem (a strengthened version) there exists a stopping time $T \geq \zeta_M$ such that $T > \zeta_M$ wherever $\zeta_M < +\infty$, and a solution Y of SDE on M in $[\zeta_M, T]$ with initial value X_{ζ_M} on $\{\zeta_M < \zeta\}$ and a constant $\in M$ elsewhere. Thus X and Y are both solutions of SDE on E in $A = [\zeta_M, T \wedge \zeta] \cap (\bar{\mathbb{R}}_+ \times \{\zeta_M < \zeta\})$ which coincide at time ζ_M on $\{\zeta_M < \zeta\}$. By a uniqueness theorem (in E) they coincide throughout A. In other words $X \in M$ still on A, which by the definition of ζ_M implies that A is empty and $\zeta_M = \zeta$. □

To summarize, we have seen that if we embed M, a $C^{2,1}$ manifold, as a closed submanifold of E, a finite dimensional real vector space, then any SDE on M can be extended to one on E, and that the solution in E stays in M if the initial value of the solution belongs to M.

This allows us to transfer known results about solutions of a SDE on E to those of one on M without much difficulty. For instance, one can prove that for a given $a \in \mathcal{T}_0$ there exists a maximal predictable stopping time $\zeta > 0$ and a unique maximal solution X of SDE on $[0,\zeta[$ (which is a continuous semimartingale) such that $X_0 = a$. If $\zeta(\omega) \leq +\infty$ then as $t \to \zeta(\omega)$ $X_t(\omega) \to \infty$ (eventually doesn't return to any compact subset of M); if $\zeta(\omega) = \overline{+\infty}$ then as $t \to +\infty$ $X_t(\omega) \to$ some point of M depending on ω.

Also the last proposition is easily extended to the case where E is replaced by a $C^{2,1}$ manifold N, by embedding both into a Euclidean space E. The hypothesis that M be closed in N can be weakened to M being *continuously properly* immersed in N: if $\Phi: M \to N$ is the immersion then whenever $(x_t)_{t \in \mathbb{R}_+}$ diverges to ∞ in M then $(\Phi(x_t))_{t \in \mathbb{R}_+}$ is not convergent.

CHAPTER 11

LIFTING OF A SEMIMARTINGALE WITH RESPECT TO A CONNECTION

We begin with some basic definitions.

Let $\pi : G \to B$ be a $C^{2,1}$ *submersion* of one $C^{2,1}$ manifold G into another, B: for each $g \in G$, $\overset{1}{\pi}(g) : T^1(G,g) \to T^1(B,\pi(g))$ is surjective, so that locally $T^1(G)$ is a product of $T^1(B)$. However, locally G is not necessarily a product of B with a fixed manifold, and the *fibers* $\pi^{-1}(b)$, $b \in B$, are not necessarily homeomorphic.

Example (lima bean). G is the surface or solid in $\mathbb{R}^3$ depicted below with one end over the other, $B = \pi G$ where

π denotes the projection onto $\mathbb{R}^2$.

For each $g \in G$ the vectors in the kernel of $\overset{1}{\pi}(g)$ are called *vertical;* together they form the vertical subbundle of $T^1(G)$. A *connection* on G is a C^1 section Θ of the Grassmannian of $T^1(G)$ such that for each $g \in G$, $\Theta(g) \cap \ker \overset{1}{\pi}(g) = 0$, and moreover we shall assume that the connection is maximal in the sense that $T^1(G,g) = \Theta(g) \oplus \ker \overset{1}{\pi}(g)$. The vectors of $\Theta(g)$ are called *horizontal* with respect to Θ. Alternatively a connection is a system of linear liftings $\theta(g)$ of the quotient $\overset{1}{\pi}(g):T^1(G,g) \to T^1(B,\pi(g))$, depending in a C^1 fashion on $g \in G$: for each $g \in G$, $\theta(g):T^1(B,\pi(g)) \to T^1(G,g)$ such that $\overset{1}{\pi}(g)\theta(g) = id_{T^1(B,\pi(g))}$. The link between the two points of view is simply $\Theta(g) = \mathrm{Im}\,\theta(g)$.

We say that a C^1 deterministic curve X in G is horizontal with respect to the connection Θ; or a solution of Θ, if for each $t, \frac{d}{dt} X(t) \in \Theta(X(t))$. A C^1 curve $\hat{X}$ in G is called a horizontal lifting of a curve X in B if $\hat{X}$ is horizontal with respect to Θ and $\pi\hat{X} = X$; X is necessarily C^1. Conversely, any C^1 curve X in B and in the range of π, admits horizontal liftings with respect to Θ. Indeed we can embed $B \hookrightarrow E$ a Euclidean space where the orthogonal projection $p:B\times E \hookrightarrow T^1(B)$ is given at $(b,v) \in B\times E$ by $p(b,v)$ = orthogonal projection of v onto $T^1(B,b) \subset E$. Then we have in $H(b,t) := p(b, \frac{d}{dt} X(t))$ a time-dependent C^0 vector field H on B such that $H(X(t),t) = \frac{d}{dt} X(t)$. Now $\hat{X}$ can be given locally as follows. Choose a point $\hat{X}_0 \in G$ such that $\pi\hat{X}_0 = X(0)$. Then a solution $\hat{X}$ of the lifted O.D.E. $\frac{d}{dt}\hat{X}(t) = \theta(\hat{X}(t))H(\pi\hat{X}(t),t)$ with $X(0) = \hat{X}_0$ fulfills the requirements.

In this section we shall outline the second order analogue of the converse above in the stochastic case where X is a continuous B-semimartingale.

Before commencing we recall the vocabulary and notation for the special case where G is a $C^{2,1}$ *fiber bundle* over B with fiber type F. This means that G,B, and F are $C^{2,1}$ manifolds (F not necessarily connected though), and a $C^{2,1}$ projection $\pi: G \to B$ is given, with the following property: for each $b \in B$ there exist an open neighbourhood B_1 of b in B, and a diffeomorphism Φ from $B_1 \times F$ onto $\pi^{-1}(B_1)$ such that for every $b_1 \in B_1$, $\Phi(b_1,.)$ is a diffeomorphism of F onto $\pi^{-1}(b_1)$. (Thus all fibers $\pi^{-1}(b)$, $b \in B$, are diffeomorphic to F.) G is said to be a $C^{2,1}$ vector bundle over B with fiber type F, if F and all the $\pi^{-1}(b)$, $b \in B$, are given as vector spaces and if there exists Φ, as above, with each $\Phi(b_1,.)$: $F \to \pi^{-1}(b_1)$, $b_i \in B_1$, a linear isomorphism.

A connection on a fiber bundle G then looks locally (taking coordinates, i.e. assume G,B, and F are vector spaces) like the graph of a $C^{1,1}$ function Γ: with $G = B \times F$, $g \in G$ written as $g = (b,f)$ and $\Theta(g) = \mathrm{Im}\,\theta(g)$ where $\theta(g) \in \mathcal{L}(B, B \oplus F)$, then $\theta(b,f) = id_B \oplus \Gamma(b,f)$ where $\Gamma(b,f) \in \mathcal{L}(B,F)$. When G is a vector bundle we say that the connection is linear in the case that for every local representation of θ, Γ is linear in the fiber F i.e. $\Gamma(b,f) = \Gamma(b)f$ where $\Gamma(b)$ belongs to $\mathcal{L}(F,\mathcal{L}(B,F)) = \mathcal{L}_2(B\times F,F)$. (Writing things out with respect to bases leads to the Christoffel symbols of classical differential geometry.)

Returning to the business at hand, we state the following theorem which enables us to give a definition of a horizontal semimartingale with respect to a connection.

<u>Theorem</u>. Let M be a C^2 (respectively $C^{2,1}$) manifold, Θ any C^1 (resp. $C^{1,1}$) d-dimensional section of the Grassmannian of $T^1(M)$ ($d=\dim\Theta(x) \leq \dim M$), and $\bar{\Theta}(x)$ the smallest vector subspace of $T^2(M,x)$ containing the complete accelerations of C^2 curves in M whose tangents belong to Θ . Then $\bar{\Theta}$ is a C^0 (resp. $C^{0,1}$) section of the Grassmannian of $T^2(M)$; $\dim\bar{\Theta}(x) = d+d(d+1)/2$. Alternately $\bar{\Theta}(x)$ is characterized as being the smallest subspace of $T^2(M,x)$ containing the vectors

(1°) $(\xi\eta+\eta\xi)(x)$ where ξ,η are arbitrary C^1 vector fields on M such that $\xi(y), \eta(y) \in \Theta(y)$ for all $y \in M$;

or equivalently:

(2°) $\xi^2(x)$ where ξ is an arbitrary C^1 vector field on M such that $\xi(y) \in \Theta$ for all $y \in M$.

Moreover, $\bar{\Theta} \cap T^1(M) = \Theta$ and under $T^2(M)/T^1(M) \approx T^1(M)\odot T^1(M)$ $\bar{\Theta}/\Theta$ is carried onto $\Theta\odot\Theta$. In the case that $M = G$ where $\pi : G \to B$ is a C^2 (resp. $C^{2,1}$) surjective submersion and Θ is a C^1 (resp. $C^{1,1}$) connection arising as $\mathrm{Im}\,\theta$, then $\bar{\Theta}(g)=\mathrm{Im}\,\bar{\theta}(y)$

where $\bar{\theta}(g): T^2(B,\pi g) \to T^2(G,g)$ is a linear lifting of $\overset{2}{\pi}(g)$ i.e. $\overset{2}{\pi}(g)\bar{\theta}(g) = \mathrm{id}_{T^2(B,\pi(g))}$; θ is C^0 (resp. $C^{0,1}$). (Thus $\bar{\Theta}$ is a second order connection). Also $\bar{\theta}(g)|_{T^1(B,\pi(g))} = \theta(g)$ and $\bar{\theta}(g)$ acts on $T^2(B,\pi(g))/T^1(B,\pi(g)) = T^1(B,\pi(g)) \odot T^1(B,\pi(g))$ into $T^2(G,g)/T^1(G,g) = T^1(G,g) \odot T^1(G,g)$ as $\theta(g) \odot \theta(g)$, i.e. the following diagram commutes ($b = \pi(g)$):

$$\begin{array}{ccccc} T^2(B,b)/T^1(B,b) & \xrightarrow{\bar{\theta}(g)} & \bar{\Theta}(g)/\Theta(g) & \hookrightarrow & T^2(G,g)/T^1(G,g) \\ \wr\| & & \| & & \| \\ T^1(B,b)\odot T^1(B,b) & \xrightarrow[\theta(g)\odot\theta(g)]{} & \Theta(g)\odot\Theta(g) & \hookrightarrow & T^1(G,g)\odot T^1(G,g) \end{array}$$

If further, G is a fiber bundle over B then locally $\bar{\Theta}$ is the graph of a function $\bar{\Gamma}$, which is linear in the fiber variable if G is a vector bundle and the connection is linear.

<u>Definition</u>. Let $\pi: G \to B$ be a C^2 submersion and Θ a C^1 connection on G. A continuous G-semimartingale $\hat{X}$ is called horizontal with respect to Θ if $\tau(d\underline{\hat{X}}) \subset \bar{\Theta}(\hat{X})$ $d\underline{\hat{X}}$-a.e. (see the section on the tangent space to a semimartingale). $\hat{X}$ is then called a horizontal lifting of $X := \pi\hat{X}$ with respect to Θ.

Note that since $\overset{2}{\pi}\bar{\theta} = \mathrm{id}$, $\bar{\theta}\overset{2}{\pi}$ is the projection of $T^2(G)$ onto $\bar{\Theta}$. Thus since $\bar{\Theta} = \mathrm{Im}\bar{\theta}\overset{2}{\pi} = \ker(I-\bar{\theta}\overset{2}{\pi})$, $\tau(d\underline{\hat{X}}) \subset \bar{\Theta}(\hat{X})$ $d\underline{\hat{X}}$-a.e., iff $\tau(d\underline{\hat{X}}) \subset \ker(I-\bar{\theta}\overset{2}{\pi})$ $d\underline{\hat{X}}$-a.e. iff $(I-\bar{\theta}\overset{2}{\pi})d\underline{\hat{X}} = 0$ $d\underline{\hat{X}}$-a.e. iff $d\underline{\hat{X}} = \bar{\theta}\overset{2}{\pi}d\underline{X}$. Therefore, with $X = \pi\hat{X}$, a B-semimartingale: $\hat{X}$ is horizontal with respect to Θ iff $d\underline{\hat{X}} = \bar{\theta}(X)\overset{2}{\pi}(\hat{X})d\underline{\hat{X}}$, $d\hat{X}$-a.e. or equivalently $d\underline{\hat{X}} = \bar{\theta}(\hat{X})d\underline{X}$, $d\hat{X}$-a.e..

Suppose now that we have a SDE on B defined by the first and second order vector fields $(H_k)_{k=1}^n$ and $(H_{ij})_{1\le i,j\le m}$ respectively, and real-valued semimartingales $(Z^k)_{k=1}^m$. Then we can lift SDE to a stochastic differential equation $\widehat{SDE}$ on G via the lifted-vector fields $(\hat{H}_k)_{k=1}^m$ and $(\hat{H}_{ij})_{1\le i,j\le m}$, and the same semimartingales $(Z^k)_{k=1}^m$, where $\hat{H}_k(g) = \theta(g)H_k(\pi(g))$ and $\hat{H}_{ij}(g) = \bar{\theta}(g)H_{ij}(\pi g)$. Indeed by the previous theorem the image of $\hat{H}_{ij}(g)$ in $T^1(G,g)\odot T^1(G,g) = T^2(G,g)/T^1(G,g)$ is $\theta(g)\circledcirc\theta(g)\ (H_i(\pi(g))\odot H_j(\pi(g))) = [\theta(g)H_i(\pi(g))]\odot[\theta(g)H_j(\pi(g))] = H_i(g)\odot H_j(g)$. If SDE is locally Lipschitz then so is $\widehat{SDE}$, assuming that Θ is $C^{1,1}$.

If X is any solution of SDE on B and $\hat{X}$ is a continuous G-semimartingale over X ($\pi\hat{X} = X$), then $\hat{X}$ is horizontal with respect to Θ iff $d\underline{\hat{X}} = \bar{\theta}(\hat{X})d\underline{X}$; but $\theta(\hat{X})$ carries tangential representations of $d\underline{X}$ into ones for $d\underline{\hat{X}}$ by operating on the vector fields. In our case:

$$d\underline{X} = \sum_k H_k(X)dZ^k + \frac{1}{2}\sum_{i,j} H_{ij}(X)d[Z^i,Z^j]$$

so

$$\bar{\theta}(\hat{X})d\underline{X} = \sum_k \bar{\theta}(X)H_k(X)dZ^k + \frac{1}{2}\sum_{i,j} \bar{\theta}(\hat{X})H_{ij}(X)d[Z^i,Z^j]$$

$$= \sum_k \hat{H}_k(\hat{X})dZ^k + \frac{1}{2}\sum_{i,j} \hat{H}_{ij}(\hat{X})d[Z^i,Z^j].$$

Thus we have established the following important result.

Proposition. Let $\pi: G \to B$ be a submersion and Θ a connection. If X, a B-semimartingale, is a solution of SDE, and $\hat{X}$ is a continuous G-semimartingale over X then $\hat{X}$ is horizontal with respect to Θ iff $\hat{X}$ is a solution of $\widehat{\text{SDE}}$.

We have seen in the last section that every continuous semimartingale is the solution of at least one SDE, therefore we have the first part of the following proposition.

Proposition. Let $\pi: G \to B$ be a $C^{2,1}$ surjective submersion between $C^{2,1}$ manifolds and Θ a $C^{1,1}$ connection on G. Let X be a continuous B-semimartingale and $\hat{a}_0 \in \mathcal{T}_0$ in G with $\pi\hat{a} = a := X_0$. Then X admits a unique maximal horizontal lifting $\hat{X}$ with respect to Θ on $[0,\hat{\zeta}[$, where $\hat{\zeta} > 0$ is a predictable stopping time, and such that $\hat{X}_0 = \hat{a}$. If X satisfies some SDE then $\hat{X}$ satisfies $\widehat{\text{SDE}}$ with initial value $\hat{a}$. Furthermore if either G is a fiber bundle over B such that each connected component of each fiber is compact (in particular if each fiber is compact or discrete), or G is a vector bundle over B with Θ a linear connection, then $\hat{\zeta} = \overline{+\infty}$.

REFERENCES

Dellacherie, C., Meyer, P.-A., *Probabilités et potentiel*, Paris, Hermann, Vol. 1,2, 1975.

Meyer, P.-A., *Un cours sur les intégrales stochastiques*, Séminaire de probabilités X, Strasbourg 1974-75. Lecture Notes in Mathematics No. 511, pp. 246-400, Berlin, Heidelberg, New York, Springer Verlag, 1976.

Schwartz, L., *Semi-martingales sur des variétés, et martingales conformes sur des variétés analytiques complexes*, Lecture Notes in Mathematics No. 780, Berlin, Heidelberg, New York, Springer Verlag, 1980.

Schwartz, L., *les Semi-martingales formelles*, Séminaire de probabilités XV 1979-80, Lecture Notes in Mathematics No.850, pp.413-489, Berlin, Heidelberg, New York, Springer Verlag, 1981.

Schwartz, L., *Géométrie différentielle du deuxième ordre, semi-martingales et équations différentielles stochastiques sur une variété*, Séminaire de probabilités XVI, 1980-81, Supplément: *Géométrie différentielle stochastique*, Lecture Notes in Mathematics No. 921, pp. 1-150, Berlin, Heidelberg, New York, Springer Verlag, 1982.

INDEX OF DEFINED TERMS
(IN ALPHABETICAL ORDER)

INDEX OF SYMBOLS

(IN ORDER OF FIRST OCCURRENCE)

LES PRESSES DE L'UNIVERSITÉ DE MONTRÉAL
C.P. 6128, succ. « A », Montréal (Québec), Canada H3C 3J7

EXTRAIT DU CATALOGUE

Mathématiques

COLLECTION « SÉMINAIRE DE MATHÉMATIQUES SUPÉRIEURES »

57. **Minimal Varieties in Real and Complex Geometry.** H. Blaine LAWSON, Jr
58. **La Théorie des points fixes et ses applications à l'analyse.** Kazimierz GEBA, Karol BORSUK, Andrzej JANKOWSKI et Edward ZHENDER
59. **Numerical Analysis of the Finite Element Method.** Philippe G. CIARLET
60. **Méthodes numériques en mathématiques appliquées.** J.F. Giles AUCHMUTY, Michel CROUZEIX, Pierre JAMET, Colette LEBAUD, Pierre LESAINT et Bertrand MERCIER
61. **Analyse numérique matricielle.** Paul ARMINJON
62. **Problèmes d'optimisation en calcul des probabilités.** Serge DUBUC
63. **Chaînes de Markov sur les permutations.** Gérard LETAC
64. **Géométrie différentielle stochastique.** Paul MALLIAVIN
65. **Numerical Methods for Solving Time-Dependent Problems for Partial Differential Equations.** Heinz-Otto KREISS
66. **Difference Sets in Elementary Abelian Groups.** Paul CAMION
67. **Groups in Physics : Collective Model of the Nucleus; Canonical Transformation in Quantum Mechanics.** Marcos MOSHINSKY
68. **Points fixes pour les applications compactes : espaces de Lefschetz et la théorie de l'indice.** Andrzej GRANAS
69. **Set Theoretic Methods in Homological Algebra and Abelian Groups.** Paul EKLOF
70. **Abelian p-Groups and Mixed Groups.** Laszlo FUCHS
71. **Integral Representations and Structure of Finite Group Rings.** Klaus W. ROGGENKAMP
72. **Homological Invariants of Modules over Commutative Rings.** Paul ROBERTS
73. **Representations of Valued Graphs.** Vlastimil DLAB
74. **Groupes abéliens sans torsion.** Khalid BENABDALLAH
75. **Lie Groups, Lie Algebras and Representation Theory.** Hans ZASSENHAUS
76. **Birational Geometry for Open Varieties.** Shigeru IITAKA
77. **Lectures on Hilbert Modular Surfaces.** Friedrich HIRZEBRUCH, Gerard van der GEER
78. **Complex Geometry in Mathematical Physics.** R.O. WELLS, Jr
79. **Lectures on Approximation and Value Distribution.** Tord GANELIUS, Walter K. HAYMAN, Donald J. NEWMAN
80. **Sur la topologie des surfaces complexes compactes.** Srinivasacharyulu KILAMBI, Gottfried BARTHEL, Ludger KAUP
81. **Topics in Polynomial and Rational Interpolation and Approximation.** Richard S. VARGA
82. **Approximation uniforme qualitative sur des ensembles non bornés.** Paul M. GAUTHIER, Walter HENGARTNER
83. **Convolutions in Geometric Function Theory.** Stephan RUSCHEWEYH.
84. **Characteristic Properties of Quasidisks.** Frederik W. GEHRING
85. **Curves in Projective Space.** Joe HARRIS.
86. **Les Inégalités de Markoff et de Bernstein.** Qazi Ibadur RAHMAN, Gerhard SCHMEISSER
87. **Analyse des données.** Francis CAILLIEZ

Achevé d'imprimer en juin 1984 sur les presses des Ateliers Graphiques Marc Veilleux Inc.
Cap-Saint-Ignace, Qué.